Better Designs In Half the Time

Implementing QFD
Quality Function Deployment
in America

Third Edition

by
Bob King

GOAL/QPC

Foreword by Yoji Akao
Tamagawa University, Tokyo, Japan

Better Designs in Half the Time
published by GOAL/QPC

13 Branch Street
Methuen, MA 01844

(508) 685-3900

$34.95   paper bound
$44.95   hard bound

Volume discounts available on request

ISBN-1-879364-01-8

printing
10 9 8 7 6 5 4

THIRD EDITION
1989

Dedication

To my loving wife Ellen

without whose encouragement
and support this book
would never have been finished.

To Yoji Akao

Tamagawa University
Tokyo, Japan

my patient and generous teacher
in the many facets of Quality Function Deployment

FOREWORD

This is the first book on Quality Function Deployment to be published in the United States. I am very happy to be able to write a few words of introduction for my dear friend, Bob King. I first met Bob King in 1985. He had started to study QFD two years before that, the year (1983) in which I conducted, in Chicago, the very first seminar on that topic in the U.S. He is thus a pioneer in the field, having been one of the very first to take up its study in the U.S. What's more, it is a wonder that, after just five years of study, he should be able to write a fine book like this. I have but the greatest admiration for him.

One of the features of this book, absent in books on QFD in Japan, is the cookbook style it adopts, to spell out in a very clear manner the procedures involved in QFD. Most books in Japan, including my own, are difficult to understand. By contrast, this book is very easy to understand. It is the aim of QFD to emphasize the users' needs. This book certainly addresses the needs of the readers. Even those new to the field should be able to understand what QFD is about by studying it step-by-step according to its presentation in this book. Furthermore, this book is not a simple review of QFD in Japan. It has the added feature in that various extensions are attempted.

It was in 1966 that I first proposed the concept of QFD. The idea was born out of the need to find a way to get the production units to grasp the notions of quality assurance at the stage of planning even before going into production of new goods. In 1972, I introduced the idea of "quality deployment" and how to go about it, based on the efforts to try it out in several companies. I could not, however, come up with the best way to set up quality control in planning until I hit upon the idea of the quality control chart introduced subsequently at the Kobe Shipyard of Mitsubishi Heavy Industries.

After years of development, we could finally put together a book on "Quality Function Deployment" in 1978, under the co-editorship of Mizuno and Akao. Since then, the idea has diffused rapidly as it has been adopted by many companies including the Toyota Auto Body Company, a company well known even in the United States. This year saw the publication in Japan of many books on QFD, including its extensions into technology deployment, cost deployment, reliability deployment, etc.

Bob King includes these new extensions in his book. Readers, therefore, can learn about the most recent developments in QFD. I would like them actively to take up QFD upon studying this book and possibly refer later to my book that is likely to be translated into English soon.

I hope that, with the publication of this book, the adoption of QFD does spread in the U.S. and contribute to the improvement of the quality of American products.

August 30, 1988
Yoji Akao
Tamagawa University
Tokyo, Japan

Table of Contents

Preface
Acknowledgements

Chapter 1	Introduction	1-1
Chapter 2	How QFD Works	2-1
Chapter 3	Listening to the Customer	3-1
Chapter 4	Chart A Customer Demands/ Quality Characteristics	4-1
Chapter 5	Chart A Quality Characteristics/ Function	5-1
Chapter 6	Chart A-3 Quality Characteristics/ Quality Characteristics	6-1
Chapter 7	Chart A-4 Quality Characteristics/ Parts	7-1
Chapter 8	Chart B-1 Function/Customer Demands	8-1
Chapter 9	Chart B-2 Cost	9-1
Chapter 10	Chart B-3 Breakthrough Targets	10-1
Chapter 11	Chart B-4 Quality Plan/Critical Parts	11-1
Chapter 12	Chart C-1 Mechanisms/New Technology	12-1
Chapter 13	Chart C-2 Mechanisms/Functions	13-1
Chapter 14	Chart C-3 Mechanisms/ Quality Characteristics	14-1
Chapter 15	Chart C-4 Mechanisms/Parts	15-1
Chapter 16	Chard D-1 Failure Modes/Customer Demands	16-1
Chapter 17	Chart D-2 Failure Modes/Functions	17-1
Chapter 18	Chart D-3 Failure Modes/ Quality Characteristics	18-1
Chapter 19	Chart D-4 Parts Failure Modes/Parts	19-1
Chapter 20	Chart E-1 New Concepts/Customer Demands	20-1
Chapter 21	Chart E-2 New Concepts/Functions	21-1
Chapter 22	Chart E-3 New Concepts/ Quality Characteristics	22-1
Chapter 23	Chart E-4 New Concepts/Summary	23-1
Chapter 24	Chart F-1 Cost Breakthroughs/Value Engineering	24-1
Chapter 25	Chart F-2 FTA/Reliability Breakthroughs	25-1
Chapter 26	Chart F-3 Reviewed Dendrogram	26-1
Chapter 27	Chart F-4 Design Improvement Plan	27-1
Chapter 28	Chart G-1 QA Table	28-3
Chapter 29	Chart G-2 Equipment Deployment	29-1
Chapter 30	Chart G-3 QC Process Planning Chart	30-1
Chapter 31	Chart G-4 QC Process Fault Tree	31-1

Chapter 32   Chart G-5 Process FMEA Chart   32-1
Chapter 33   Chart G-6 Parts and Assembly   33-1
Chapter 34   Implementation   34-1

Appendix A The Seven New Tools

PREFACE

This book is for a variety of audiences; please see inside the front cover for suggestions for the beginning, intermediate and advanced students of Quality Function Deployment.

It is based on the works of Japan's leading Quality Function Deployment expert and teacher, Yoji Akao. [1] [2] Dr. Akao is vice-president of the Japan Society for Quality Control and professor of industrial engineering at Tamagawa, University in Tokyo. As chairman of the JSQC QFD research committee from 1975 to 1986, it was his responsibility to develop QFD and promote its usage in Japan. What he did is develop a comprehensive system with all the options.

---

[1]   Shigeru Mizuno and Yoji Akao (1978): "Quality Function Deployment - An Approach to CWQC", J.U.S.E.

[2]   Yoji Akao (1987): "Quality Function Deployment", JSA

Those preferring a more basic approach are referred to the work of Macabe, a Japanese reliability engineer who teaches QFD in basically four matrices:

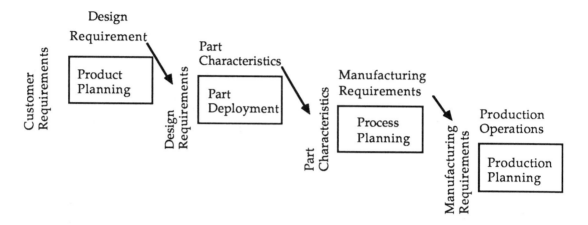

An excellent basic approach is also taught by Fukahara of the Central Japan Quality Control Association. He focuses heavily on the House of Quality which compares customers' demands with quality characteristics and quality characteristics with each other (the roof of the house). He also teaches a number of variations on that theme.[3]

Yoji Akao was appointed chairman of the QFD Research Committee of JSQC (Japan Society for Quality Control) in the early 1970's and held that post until 1987 when the promotion of QFD was successfully completed and the committee was disbanded. In that capacity Akao researched all published QFD studies and tried to integrate the contribution of each into one comprehensive system. He is the sole teacher of this QFD system for JUSE (Union of Japanese Scientists and Engineers), JSA (Japan Standards Association) and many other leading Japanese quality organizations.

---

[3]   The American Supplier Institute in Dearborn, Michigan offers regular courses on these clear and powerful approaches.

Based on the Akao tradition, this book covers voice of the customer, value engineering, reliability, new technology, bottleneck engineering, FMEA, PDPC (Process Decision Program Chart) and other disciplines that Akao integrates in his approach to QFD. The author has further expanded that matrix as illustrated on the following page.

This book does make three important changes from Akao.
(1) In Japan, many subjects are taught in puzzle form and the student learns by solving the puzzle. This book is the result of two years' effort changing puzzles to the cookbook approach. There is one chapter on each chart; after the description of the chart is:

a)   statement of purpose
b)   inputs and outputs
c)   history
d)   significance for design
e)   simple example
f)   step by step method for filling out
       with coded numbers on blank charts
g)   blank chart for practice

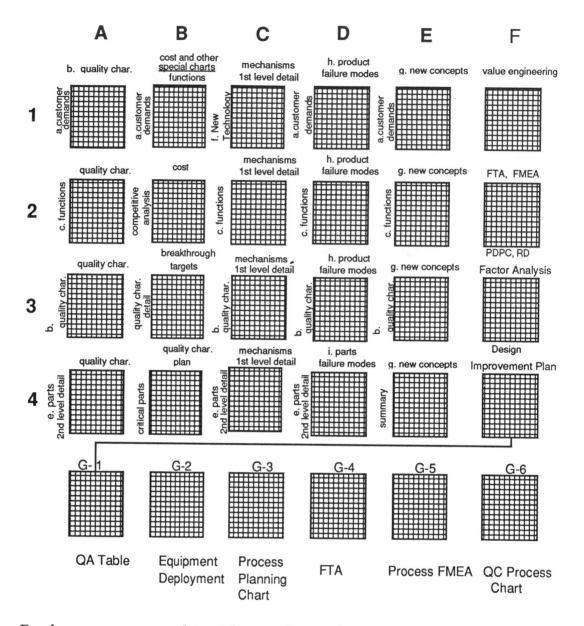

Readers are encouraged to pick a product, software or service they are familiar with and practice filling out charts as they read. This will facilitate understanding and absorption of the concepts and procedures.

(2) This book differs from the Akao approach in that it includes the New Concept Selection Methods of Stuart Pugh of Scotland. Some have suggested that the strength of the Japanese system is taking a particular technology and improving reliability and reducing cost. The addition of Pugh's New Concept Selection assures a fresh look at the product.

(3) The arrangement of charts, though it includes all charts in the Akao system, differs slightly. Many QFD practitioners have requested a system that they can fill out row by row, top to bottom. So the charts are labeled by column and row and read A1, A2, A3, A4, B1, B2, B3, B4, C1, etc.

This is not a system to be copied. This is the full QFD tool kit. Readers and practitioners are encouraged to pick charts that will help them with real problems or implement actual company strategies. The following list indicates some of the purposes of QFD and what it will help do:

1)   Listening to voice of customer
2)   Improving horizontal communication
3)   Prioritizing improvements
4)   Targeting cost reduction
5)   Targeting reliability
6)   Targeting engineering breakthroughs
7)   Orchestrating engineering breakthroughs
8)   Improving communication between design and manufacturing
9)   Process reliability

Some find it helpful to consider which charts need to be done in what order. The following table may help.

Some find it difficult to take on QFD without a preconception of design-related phases. If that sounds like your temperament, you might consider reading the book in this order.
1) Background Chapters 1 and 2
2) Phase 1   Clarify Voice of Customers
    Chapter 3   customer research
          4   customer demands/
                quality characteristics

          8   customer demands/functions
          12   customer demands/product
                failures
          16   customer demands/New Concepts
3) Phase 2   Defining product based on
             opportunities, obstacles, and possible
             breakthroughs.
     A2, A3, A4   Chapters 5- 7
     B2, B3, B4   Chapters 9-11
     C2, C3, C4   Chapters 12-15
     D2, D3, D4   Chapters 17-19
     E2, E3, E4   Chapters 21-23

4) Phase 3   Achieving and describing product
             breakthrough.
     F1 - 4   Chapters 24-27

5) Phase 4   Achieving and describing process
             breakthrough
     G1 - 6   Chapters 28-33

6) Implementation Models/Organization
                 Chapter 34

Hopefully this format will help most readers to achieve significant breakthrough in hardware, software, and service.

Any suggestions are most welcome - and will be considered for inclusion in future editions.

The author's greatest concern about releasing this book is that people who know little about Japanese management will pick up this book and try to use its methods in isolation from other management systems. The following chart is an attempt to show QFD's relation to other management/quality systems.

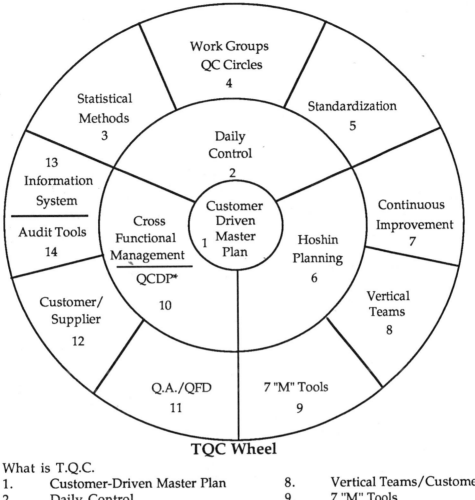

TQC Wheel

What is T.Q.C.

1.	Customer-Driven Master Plan	8.	Vertical Teams/Customer
2.	Daily Control	9.	7 "M" Tools
3.	Statistical Methods	10.	Cross-Functional Mgmt.
4.	Work Groups/QC Circles	11.	QA/QFD
5.	Standardization	12.	Horizontal Teams-QCDP
6.	Hoshin Planning	13.	Information Systems
7.	Continuous Improvement	14.	Audit Tools

*Quality, Cost, Delivery, Profit (or Product)

TQM Vision

1.   **Imagine** an organization that knows what customers will want 5-10 years from now and exactly what they will do to far exceed all expectations.

2.   **Imagine** an organization where each employee knows what he needs to do to make the organization run smoothly. His actions are documented, audited, and updated daily as changing situations require.

3.   **Imagine** an organization where each employee manages by facts and knows how to analyze problems by using simple tools to understandvariability and data.

4.   **Imagine** an organization where each employee generates 100-200 suggestions per year (2-4 per week), of which 95% is implemented, and joins with the work groups to maximize progress.

5.   **Imagine** an organization where everybody knows the most important variables to control in order to satisfy customers, guarantee effectiveness and efficiency, and where these standards are documented and updated daily.

6.   **Imagine** an organization where the president sets the two or three most important goals for the year, every manager knows these goals, and the two or three most important tasks to help achieve these goals, and each manager has measurable milestones for these activities which he personally audits monthly, documents, and sends up through the organization to enable diagnosis and improvement.

7.   **Imagine** an organization where each employee understands not only how to do his job but also how to significantly improve his job on a regular basis.

8.   **Imagine** an organization where all problems and challenges are met by a team of the most appropriate people, regardless of their levels or jobs within the organization.

9.   **Imagine** an organization where all managers and staff people use effective and simple planning tools on a regular basis to do a better job.

10.   **Imagine** an organization where cross-functional teams assure that quality, cost, efficiency, services, and profit are managed on a consistently high level throughout each business unit of the organization.

11.   **Imagine** an organization where quality assurance and reliability are managed effectively on a daily basis and the total organization is thoroughly familiar with customers.

12.   **Imagine** an organization where each employee knows all the people who supply him or her with data and material

and gives these people clear, concise advice on how to improve that data and material and also where each person knows all his customers and seeks ways to meet expectations in providing data and material.

13.   **Imagine** an organization where all information smoothly and concisely flows daily to the people who need it.

14.   **Imagine** an organization where improvement activities are audited at each level of the organization to assure that each employee reaches his or her full potential.

QFD then is a relatively small part of a very large system. Hopefully the readers of this text will be able to use this tool to satisfy more customers and thereby increase their market share.

ACKNOWLEDGEMENTS

Many people have contributed either directly or indirectly to this book. Some of them include:

Robert Adams and Mark Gavoor of Rockwell International for proofing an early edition of the book and for making many helpful suggestions to improve it;

Yoji Akao of Tamagawa University, Tokyo, for helping the author understand the width and breadth of Quality Deployment in Japan and especially for his matrix of matrices integrating the voice of the customer with reliability, factor analysis, value engineering, bottleneck engineering, new technology and other important product and process improvement tools;

Ed Baker, Manager of Statistical Methods at Ford Motor Company for explaining the significance of alternate weighting systems in Q.F.D. and suggesting the benefits of changing from a 1-3-5 system to a 1-3-9 system;

Georgette Beaulieu of the GOAL/QPC staff for typesetting the Appendix and helping with corrections;

Pat Blodgett of the GOAL/QPC staff for inputting large sections of the book, proofing and correcting many mistakes;

Michael Brassard of the GOAL/QPC staff for significant contributions to the Appendix both in terms of Seven Management Tools instructions and examples;

John Bros and Herm Wadke of FORD Climate Control for the opportunity to work with numerous suppliers large and small and many fine suggestions on how to incorporate FORD's excellent methods into Q.F.D.;

Larry Byars of Buehler for evidence of a U.S. company using Q.F.D. to achieve a better product (climate control actuator) with less than fifty per cent of the engineering hours that would have been used without Q.F.D.;

Eva Chen of International Business Machines (Rohm Division) for undertaking one of the first Deming Prize audits in the U.S. and for helping to show how large aspects of the Japanese T.Q.C. system can work effectively in the U.S.;

Don Clausing, formerly of Xerox and now of Massachusetts Institute of Technology in Cambridge, MA., for possible tie-ins between Q.F.D., Taguchi's fractional factorial and Stuart Pugh's New Concept Selection;

Lou Cohen of Digital Equipment Corporation for good insights into how to introduce Q.F.D. and how to use Q.F.D. to improve a staff organization;

W. Edwards Deming, Statistician, Washington, DC, for details regarding the roots of Japan's economic miracle and for describing management's new job through his fourteen points;

Russ Doane of Digital Equipment Corporation for insights on how to successfully introduce the Seven Management Tools into an organization;

Aaron Feuerstein of Malden Mills, Lawrence, MA., for highlighting the value of improved communication between R&D, manufacturing and marketing, and the weakness of existing systems to accomplish this, also for providing support, especially during the early research for this book;

Tim Fuller and his staff at Hewlett Packard in Sunnyvale, CA., for suggesting the use of pencil as a Q.F.D. case study and for many other suggestions for refining the materials;

John Hauser of MIT Sloan School and Harvard Business School for current practices in customer research;

Victoria Hudson of General Motors Advanced Engineering Staff for evidence of how Q.F.D. can work in the U.S. in something as complicated as a total automobile study;

Hughes Aircraft for information on value engineering techniques;

Joseph Juran of Juran Institute, Stamford,CT., for the effective use of project teams and cross functional management;

Noriaki Kano of Tokyo Rika University, for insights into the voice of the customer, especially the distinction between exciting, expected and one dimensional quality;

Henry Klein, an independent consultant (formerly of Black and Decker), for translation of early articles on Q.F.D. and for many good probing questions on Q.F.D.;

Lawrence P. LeFebre of the GOAL/QPC staff, for designing the cover;

Glenn Mazur of Japan Business Consultants, Ltd., for an excellent job of translating much of the Japanese Q.F.D. articles into English;

Joe Myers of Sheller-Globe for being the first in the U.S. to do Q.F.D. projects using all thirty charts and showing the benefits from this approach;

John Perry and the Procter and Gamble paper products division for showing how Q.F.D. can prevent the development of products which do not meet customers' demands and how Q.F.D. can improve the interface between process engineers and manufacturing;

Bob Porter of Texas Instruments for many fine examples of Q.F.D. implementation in the metals and electronics industry;

Dale Nelson and Peter Southgate of ADC Telecommunications for Finite Element Method (FEM) as used in U.S. and Japan;

Stuart Pugh of University of Strathclyde for his New Concept Selection and possible relationships to previous and past Q.F.D. work;

Diane Ritter for proofreading and for many good suggestions regarding consistency of illustrations and labeling;

Jose Rodriguez of The Kendall Company for showing that it is both possible and desirable for a U.S. company to implement Q.F.D. as a system;

Phil Ross of General Motors for showing real progress on many Q.F.D. studies and integrating Q.F.D. with other engineering disciplines;

Saturn Corporation engineers for many fine suggestions in integrating the House of Quality, reliability engineering and New Concept selection;

Hal Schaal of FORD Light Truck and the people at FORD Motor Company for helping fund the translation of dozens of Japanese Q.F.D. case studies into English;

Larry Shillito of Eastman Kodak in Rochester, NY, for explaining value engineering as it is practiced in the U.S. and appropriate integration with Q.F.D.;

W. Kent Sterret and the other employees of Florida Light and Power for pioneering work in implementing Japanese T.Q.C. in the U.S. and showing how Q.F.D. is part of a much larger system driven by Policy Deployment;

John Studer and the people at Procter & Gamble Lodging Services for showing how Q.F.D. can help make dramatic improvements in market share;

Larry Sullivan of the American Supplier Institute (and formerly of FORD Motor Company) for promotion of Q.F.D. and its benefits and for making available the Q.F.D. work of Fukahara of the Central Japan Quality Control Association;

Dave Taylor, President of Cirtek, for sharing the value of a company president taking charge on Q.F.D., for many fine suggestions on computerization of Q.F.D. and perhaps the most cogent list of the benefits of Q.F.D;

John Terninko of Davidson/Textron for numerous corrections from edition 1.0 and many insights for making the text clearer;

University of Madison, WI, for insights on relationship of Design and Experiments to Q.F.D.

Also, the employees of many companies have participated through course questions and case studies.

AC Spark Plug	Clark Cutter McDermott
Analog Devices	Control Data Corporation
All Steel Corporation	Davidson Rubber Textron
American Supplier Institute	Detroit Diesel
AT&T	Digital Equipment Corporation
AVM Corporation	Dow Chemical

Black and Decker
Campbell Soup
C.H. Masland & Sons
Cirtek
Exxon Chemical
Firestone Tire & Rubber
Florida Power & Light
FORD Motor Company
General Electric
General Foods
General Motors
General Tire
Granville-Phillips Company
Hercules Aerospace
Hewlett-Packard
Hogan & Associates, Inc.
Hughes Aircraft
IBM Corporation
Instrumentation Labs
Ivon Corporation
Johnson Controls, Inc.
The Kendall Company
Kingston-Warren Corporation
Lear Siegler Corporation

Eastman Kodak
Eaton Corporation
Elkhart Products
Ernst & Whinney
Long Manufacturing
McCord Winn/Textron
Mead Imaging
M. & H. Industries
3M
Monsanto Research Corp.
New Departure Hyatt
New England Power
Omark Industries
Polaroid Corporation
Quin-T Corporation
Ram Air
Rockwell International
Saturn Corporation
Sheller-Globe
Siemmens A.G.
Sterling Products
Texas Instruments
Toledo Molding & Die
Unisys

Universal Foods

Chapter 1

Introduction

Better designs in half the time. It sounds too good to be true! How is it possible?

It is true that the design process is a creative one. One easily conjures up the picture of very creative people unbounded by fetters like dress code and nine to five hours. After all, breakthroughs are unpredictable. Sometimes they come surprisingly quickly. More often than not they take a very long time. All too often breakthroughs unfortunately don't come at all. How then can it really be possible to speed up design or know that you have?

It is true that much in the design process cannot be controlled, but it is also true that we do much to unnecessarily expand the design process. Let's say two engineers are working on a sun roof of a car. One engineer develops a new seal for the sun roof that makes it possible to keep the rain out even during the worst driving rainstorm. Another engineer is working on the lever that opens and shuts the sun roof. He figures out how to simplify the design and it works well with the old seal. Neither engineer knows of the impending disaster. Maybe the problem is caught before the cars start running off the assembly line: then it means **redesign** for seal, or lever or both. Maybe it is found later when customers cannot open or shut the window with one hand. Then it involves **redesign, recall, rework.**

A customer sends a supplier specs (specifications) for a component for an air-conditioning system. The specs are incomplete or even wrong. The supplier designs the product making his best guess what the customer wants. Sometimes the supplier guesses right, sometimes he guesses wrong. If he guesses wrong, then we have **redesign** by customer and supplier.

Tire wear is a problem on a particular truck line. The tire manufacturers continually **redesign.** Perhaps steering is the problem, so the steering engineers continue to redesign. Perhaps suspension is the problem so the suspension engineers continue to redesign. The three engineering groups never come together. When they do come together they disagree on causes because they are using the same words but do not realize they have developed different meanings for those words.

Then there is job transfer. One engineer moves in the middle of a big project and another engineer takes over. There is limited documentation on the project to date. For months or years the new engineer is finding out about things the other engineer was doing. The price is **redesign** and more **redesign.**

A major design project is two thirds complete. A high executive sees a new study, listens to a complaint or, for whatever reason, decides that something is wrong. The result is a major or minor **redesign.**

Hopefully these are enough examples for the reader to supply other examples either from manufacturing or service.

One might draw a diagram of the design process as follows:

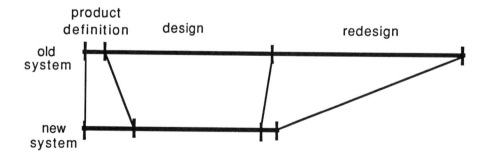

Figure 1.1 Comparison of old and new design systems

A relatively short time is spent defining the product. A relatively long time is spent designing the product and a surprisingly long time is often spent redesigning the product. The end point of redesign is all too often the mandate to start producing the product.

The key to shortening the overall design time is to better define the product and better document the design process. This improves the efficiency of the initial design and drastically reduces the need for redesign. This is referred to as *new system* in Figure 1.1.

The QFD approach *expands* the time it takes to define the product. It shortens the time it takes to design the product by focusing priorities, better documentation and communication during the process. It virtually eliminates the need for redesign, especially on critical items.

In Japan the savings from QFD have been defined thus:

In many of the cases reported, the use of quality deployment has cut in half the problems at the beginning stages, shortened development time from one-half to one-third, all the while assuring users' satisfaction and increasing sales.
Yoji Akao

Akao is in a pretty good position to evaluate the use of QFD. He has headed the JSQC (Japan Society for Quality Control) QFD Research Committee since its inception.[1] In that capacity he reviewed all published QFD case studies since the beginning of QFD in Japan in the late 1960's.[2] He also is the only instructor in QFD for JUSE and JSA and consults widely on QFD with many Japanese (and U.S.) companies.[3]

---

[1] See Akao, Yoji, ed. Quality Function Deployment. JUSE, 1978.

[2] Yoji Akao (1972): "New Product Development and Quality Assurance - Quality Deployment System Standardization and Quality Control, Vol. 25, No. 4, pp. 9-14. JSA

[3] Dr. Akao developed the first quality table in conjunction with his work at Mitsubishi Heavy Industries, Kobe Shipyard.
    Hirobaju Nishimura (1972): "Design of Ships and Quality Table", Quality Control, Vol. 23, May Special Issue, 41-16-20, JUSE.

It is the author's impression that most Japanese companies were already fairly focused in their design efforts before QFD because of the widespread use of policy deployment[4] and the seven Q.C. tools[5] in the administrative areas. In the U.S., where these tools have not been used, it seems to the author that QFD will result in even greater reductions in design time than in Japan because the U.S. starting point is slower. The author believes on the average at least a fifty percent reduction is possible.

Historical background to design delays

In most companies, large and small, the design process is never the same for two products. When five design people from one organization are asked to describe their design process, there are likely to be significant differences. Why is the product design system in such disarray? Two possibilities are the heavily departmentalized organization of most companies, and the absence of simple planning tools.

In the early 1900's, Frederick Taylor was an engineering consultant to several companies, Bethlehem Steel to name one. He observed that not every supervisor was smart enough to determine the best way to do a job. He popularized the idea of having engineers design the job and having production supervisors see to it that the job was done that way. The system was an immediate success. In the 1920's and 1930's many companies added quality control to see to it that production workers did the job the way the engineers had set it up.

---

[4]   Policy Deployment is the Japanese replacement for management by objectives (MBO). It focuses on the process rather than on results.

[5]   The Seven QC Tools were brought together in 1962 by Dr. Kaoru Ishikawa when the statistical quality control activity was expanded to include production workers. These tools include line charts, pareto charts, cause and effect diagrams, histograms, control charts, etc. They were given the name "QC" in the late 1970's when seven new planning tools were brought together.

What happened during this decade was that the educational level of supervisors and production workers improved, but we haven't changed the system. In fact we have fortified the walls and we have this great American pastime of throwing Molotov cocktails over the wall and wiping out the other department. Students laugh when this story and illustration is told--laugh because it is too painfully true.

Why is departmentalization significant for the **redesign** problem? For one thing design departments tend to send the design to manufacturing to see if they can make it. Marketing and design communicate incompletely. Different design departments in major companies rarely talk to each other, resulting in design conflicts and the need for **redesign**.

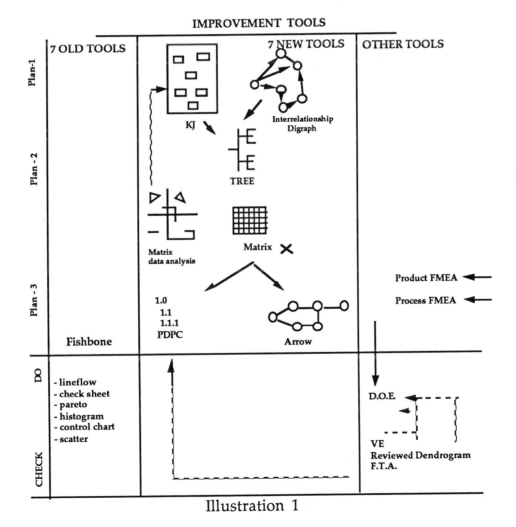

Illustration 1

Documentation and planning

One of the reasons for the success of the QFD process in Japan has been the widespread teaching of planning tools[6] throughout the organization. These planning tools, which were borrowed primarily from organizational development disciplines, became much more popular than the QFD which they support. Because these tools are so simple, people want to use them to improve their planning. Continuous improvement is seen as a cycle of plan...do...check...act (adjust).[7] The seven old tools focused on do...check...act and the seven new tools focus on improving the planning.

The **Affinity Diagram** (KJ)[8] is the first of the tools. It takes disparate language data and uses cards to rearrange the data into meaningful categories. It is very useful because often we have very different kinds of information coming from many different sources. For example, customer demands may come from surveys, complaints, warranty problems, reliability problems, etc. It is good to have a tool that helps make sense out of all that.

Affinity Chart (K-J)   Interrelationship Digraph

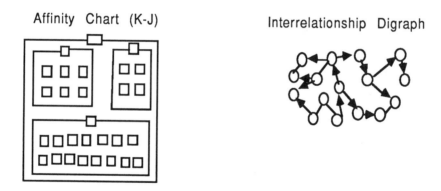

Figure 1.2 Affinity Chart and Interrelationship Digraph

---

6   Shigeru Mizuno, Editor, *Management For Quality Improvement:* The 7 New QC Tools (Cambridge, Mass.; Productivity Press, 1988), p.173.
7   This cycle is known in Japan as the Deming cycle. Dr. W. Edwards Deming gives credit to Shewhart who had the original idea.
8   KJ is the registered trademark of Jiro Kawakita for his version of the Affinity Diagram.

The **Interrelationship Digraph**, like the affinity diagram, is used for general planning. Unlike the affinity diagram, the interrelationship digraph uses the logical side of the brain. It asks which idea influences another idea and draws an arrow in the direction of the influence. It can be read by selecting the ideas that have the most arrows coming in or coming out. It can also be read by selecting the root ideas which only have items coming out of them. Like the affinity diagram its purpose is to identify meaningful categories with which to organize ideas. It is often helpful to use the first two charts in parallel with the same ideas and compare the results.

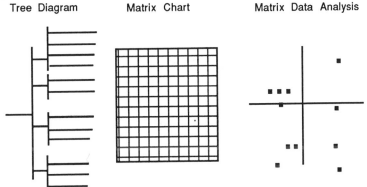

Tree Diagram   Matrix Chart   Matrix Data Analysis

Figure 1.3 Tree Diagram, Matrix Chart and Matrix
          Data Analysis

Intermediate planning

The tree diagram looks like a sideways organizational chart. It continually identifies ideas in greater and greater detail. At first the question is, "What is the major component of this idea?" Then it usually shifts to, "How will this idea be accomplished?" The tree diagram goes beyond the first two charts by assisting the thought process in identifying items which were missed in the brainstorming process for the affinity chart and the interrelationship digraph.

The **Matrix** chart is perhaps the most widely known. It takes two groups of ideas and compares them against each other to decide if there are any correlations. This forced thought process is very beneficial. In design, one of the biggest problems is that things are often forgotten. The matrix chart helps prevent that and is widely used in QFD. It is also a common practice in QFD to bound the matrix with the most detailed level of a tree diagram. This helps to organize the ideas on each side of the matrix.

The **Matrix Data Analysis Chart** is the least used of the tools and although it has been simplified it is the most difficult of the tools. The Matrix Data Analysis Chart portrays correlations on an x and y axis. In QFD it is used to portray market segmentation and to help identify what markets a company should be in and how they relate to their competition.[9]

Detailed planning

The **PDPC Chart** (Process Decision Program Chart) is modeled after the FTA (Fault Tree Analysis) Chart. Both charts map out what can go wrong in a tree form. The PDPC is different in that it lists the countermeasures for each thing that can go wrong. The PDPC is used to plan activities that have not been undertaken before. Listing everything that can go wrong enhances the possibility of a successful project. The PDPC is also something like the tree diagram. The difference is that the PDPC has a time sequence focus.

PDPC   Arrow Diagram

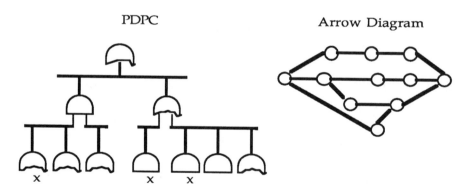

Figure 1.4   PDPC Process Decision Program Chart and
             Arrow Diagram

9   During the October, 1987 International Quality Congress in Tokyo, the author asked Nayatani about the inclusion of this chart among the Seven Management Tools (formerly called the Seven New Tools). He replied that the mathematical basis of the matrix data analysis is important and needs to be more widely understood. It was included for this reason.

The **arrow diagram** is very similar to the PERT (Program Evaluation Review Technique) or the CPM (Critical Path Method). The major difference is that it is a simplified method for widespread use in an organization. A good number of people know PERT and CPM but a relatively small segment of that group uses it because of its complexity. The arrow diagram shows parallel paths in undertaking an activity. The purpose of this is to find the shortest time possible for the project and to graphically portray what things can be done simultaneously.

In conclusion, what has happened to planning tools in the U.S. is that they have become more and more complex. As a result of that they are not widely used. There is also a minimum of planning because of the short range focus of most organizations. They are driven by meeting orders and having a good quarterly statement and short term return on investment for shareholders. This lack of planning, along with departmentalization, has contributed to some of the chaotic state of product design.

What is QFD?

QFD is a system for designing product or service based on customer demands and involving all members of the producer or supplier organization. It is sometimes referred to as the most advanced form of Total Quality Control, Japanese style,[10] which can be described by the following chart:

All employees All departments	Improving or maintaining quality cost yield procedures systems	To give customers product or service that is best qualified most useful most economic

What QFD does is add design to the improvement and maintenance activities of all employees to give customers the best product. QFD can be defined broadly or narrowly as

---

10   Joseph Juran taught the Japanese the need for manager Quality Control in 1954 and influenced their conversion from SQC into TQC. Armand Feigenbaum's use of the term Total Quality Control also helped shape Japanese thinking.

shown in the following chart.

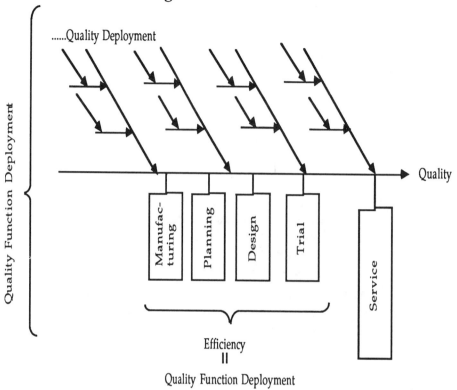

Figure 1.5   QFD Broadly and Narrowly Defined[11]

Narrowly defined, QFD refers to the organization that makes the design improvement effort possible.   Broadly defined, QFD also includes the charts that document the design process. This book will look at both aspects of QFD.

Overview of the book
This book will take a look at each of the thirty or so different QFD charts and:

describe what QFD does
describe its background
give a model filled-in chart as an example
give a step-by-step procedure to fill it out
give one or more examples of filled out charts
give exercises to practice filling out the charts

---

[11]   See Preface footnote 1.

The initial chapters will talk about how QFD fits into the design process and how to get started. The concluding chapters will describe how to use the QFD related tools and give some case studies of U.S. companies that are using QFD.

You are encouraged after reading the introduction and Chapter Two to go to the charts that most relate to your current job.

Happy exploring!

Chapter 2

How QFD Works

Even though QFD needs to be tailored to each organization, it might be helpful to consider QFD in four phases:

1. **The organization:** During this phase management selects the product or service to be improved, the appropriate interdepartmental team and defines the focus of the QFD study.

2. **The descriptive phase:** During this phase the team defines the product or service from several different directions: customer demands, functions, parts, reliability, cost, etc.

3. **The breakthrough phase:** The team selects areas for improvement and finds ways to make them better through new technology, new concepts, better reliability, cost reduction, etc. and monitors the bottleneck engineering process.

4. **The implementation phase:** The team defines the new product and how it will be manufactured. The rest of the chapter will discuss this in more detail.

Organizing the QFD project

Management has to define the product or service to be studied. This should flow naturally from the policy management system as described in Chapter 1 and the introduction. The initial project should focus on a product that already exists and is well known. This makes it possible to focus on the QFD techniques. Later projects can focus on brand new product introductions.

a. The extent of the study is important. It is possible to do a QFD study in great detail, taking months and months with much research. It is also possible to do a QFD study in a matter of days and identify targets for breakthroughs and design priorities. It is possible to learn much from one chart, e.g., the so-called quality chart or **house of quality** which compares customer demands with quality characteristics. It is

characteristics. It is also possible to do dozens of different charts with two or three iterations of each. The extent of the study varies depending on the complexity of the product and the extent of improvement that is sought.

b. Who the study is for is important. Who is requesting the study? How much funding is being provided? What is the beginning and end date? Who is being assigned to the team? QFD studies can be done by one or two people, but the effective size of the group is three to seven. What level of the organization should be involved? Who are the intended users of the study results?

c. Project selection is important. Why is the project being done? What breakthroughs are required? Are new markets being sought or is the focus expansion of existing markets? Where are the breakthroughs needed? Should the focus be broad or narrow? For example, should the study be on the whole car or just the powertrain, on door or door handle? Are we talking about a new product or a product enhancement?

d. Team is important. The ideal group is three to seven, an interdisciplinary group with people who have the needed expertise. When Ford Light Truck wanted to improve tire wear on the Ranger, they brought together a team of suspension engineers, steering engineers and tire engineers. The team should be people who want to participate, if possible. Although QFD groups have been successfully chaired by people from marketing, research and development, planning, manufacturing and quality, the largest number of groups are chaired by someone in product design. Each of the members should have a general understanding of how QFD works. The facilitator should have an in-depth understanding of QFD and the Seven New Tools.[1]

e. Statement of theme is important. It is important to state the theme up front. What is hoped to be accomplished? What tools will be used? What QFD charts will be used? How will information be shared? How will you know the project is completed?

---

[1]   Many thanks to Lawrence Shillito of Kodak for help with this section. Many of these QFD organizational concepts are parallel to ones he uses in Value Engineering and Analysis.

The Descriptive Phase

The **descriptive phase** of the project defines the product from several different perspectives. These are described as follows:

a. Customer Demands: A positive statement of **what** the customer wants and needs. It is clear enough to be understood in the same way by most people. There are often different classes of customers whose demands are recognized. For example, in making a part for a car, you might consider the assembly plant, the dealer and purchaser of the car, and have three groups of customer demands.

b. Quality Characteristics: The items that a producer controls to assure that they meet customer demands. They state **how** the producer meets demands. For example, in producing large rolls of paper it has been found that a round tube is the key to no tears or creases. So the roundness of the tube is the quality characteristic for the customer demands of wrinkle free and tear free.

c. Functions: Statements of **what the product does**. They may be like customer demands but will likely contain many key items of which only the producer is aware.

d. Mechanisms: The major **organizational sub-groups** under the focus of the QFD study. They are the first level of detail.

e. Parts: The **next level of detail** under the mechanisms. They are the second level of detail of the study.

It is sometimes difficult to understand the use of the categories, mechanisms and parts as they apply to a QFD study because they are used differently in different studies. It is possible to do a QFD study on a whole car, a major part of a car or a small component. In each of these three studies the concept of mechanism and car are used differently. The following triangle may help illustrate.

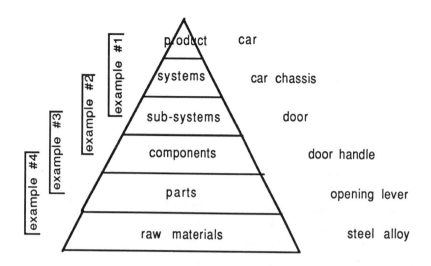

Figure 2.1 Level of Detail Chart

These four examples may help clarify the relationship between mechanism and parts:

Example #1 a. The QFD study is on the product, e.g., car
            b. The mechanisms are systems, e.g., chassis
            c. The parts are sub-systems, e.g., door

Example #2 a. The QFD study is on the car chassis
            b. The mechanisms are the sub-systems,
               e .g., door
            c.The parts are the components, e.g.,
               door handle

Example #3 a. The QFD study is on the car door
            b. The mechanisms are the components, e.g.,
               door handle
            c. The part are the parts, e.g., opening lever

Example #4 a. The QFD study is on the car door handle
            b. The mechanisms are the parts, e.g.,
               door handle
            c. The parts are the new materials

The focus of the study is determined by what product you are responsible for.

f. New Technologies: New materials that go into a product, new breakthroughs in engineering. Ideas for new technology come from trade journals, engineering schools and company central engineering or research and development groups.

g. New Concepts: New ways of thinking about the product or its parts. On a #2 lead pencil these may include pocket clip, retractable lead, and spring loaded lead.

h. Product Failure Modes: Ways in which the **product** as a whole **can fail**.

i. Parts Failure Modes: Ways in which individual parts can fail.

The Breakthrough Phase

Creativity has been described as combining two items in a new way for benefit. QFD uses the matrix system to do this. These matrices are made by combining the various categories from stage two. Looking at several of the matrices at once you get a matrix of matrices.

How these charts are used at various stages of the design process are illustrated in the Figure 2. 2.

The Implementation Phase

An informal survey of companies (QFD course participants) indicates that no two companies design products the same way. In fact many claim that in the same company no two products are designed the same way. This fluidity may account for some of the waste of time and resources in design. Certainly it makes the job of looking at the design process more difficult. Hopefully the following outline will be at once general and also specific enough for each company or service organizaton to relate to it.

In general, the development of new products may be traced in the following steps:

Product Planning
Product Design
Production Preparation
Regular Production
Sales and Service
Comprehensive Monitoring

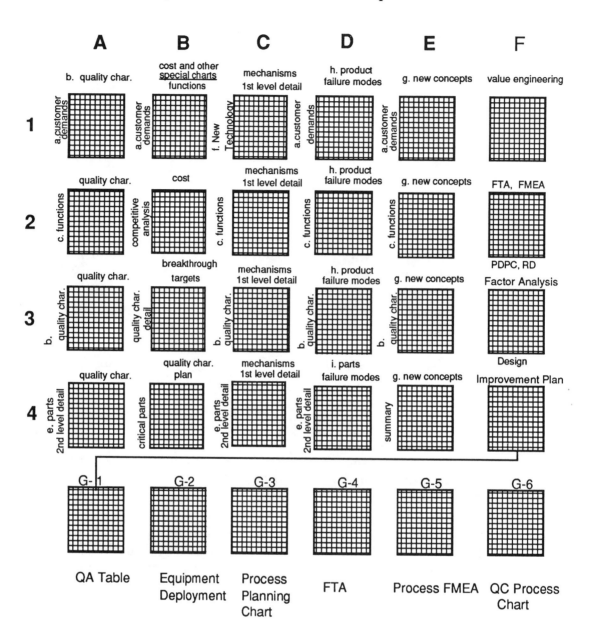

Figure 2.2 Matrix of Matrices

As indicated previously, this book takes the view that all employees have a role in each of these steps.

Product Planning has to do with deciding what business you are going to be in. It has to do with identifying existing needs and evaluating the extent to which the company or any of its competitors are meeting those needs. The workload for product planning is divided into surveying, general product planning and individual planning.

Surveying

Surveying includes gathering information about product class. The sales department is responsible for determining market requirements. Design engineering is responsible for surveying competing products and surveying patent rights. Manufacturing engineering is responsible for testing competing products. Quality Assurance is responsible for doing a preparatory study of quality requirements. All of this is overseen by a project director. This information is analyzed in the initial quality table and the matrix data analysis. This surveying activity is portrayed in Figure 2.6.

General Product Planning

The analysis of the Matrix Data Analysis (see Chapter 3) leads to an understanding of market segmentation, where a product sits in comparison to the competition and, most importantly, which product opportunities exist. These product opportunities may include the expansion of product in existing markets or new markets or the introduction of new products in existing markets or new markets. This concept is represented by the following matrix.

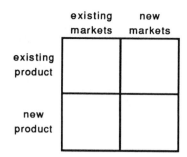

Figure 2.3 Market Expansion Grid

General Product Planning is also assisted by the analysis of the Quality Table, Chart A-1, which identifies the level of importance of each customer demand and how well the company is already meeting those demands. It identifies opportunities for sales points and investigates the critical quality characteristics. Most important, the quality table identifies the five or six key areas for breakthrough to develop a world class product, part or service. The quality table will be presented in detail in Chapter 4. The following is an illustration:

Quality Characteristics | **Quality Plan**

A-1 Pencil / Customer Demands	length	time between sharpening	lead dust generated	hexagonality	rate of importance	company now	competitor x	competitor y	plan	ratio of improvement	sales point	absolute wt.	demanded wt.
Easy to hold	O 42			O 42	3	4	3	3	4	1	1	3	14
Does not smear		O 69	⊚ 207		4	5	4	5	5	1	1.2	4.8	23
Point lasts	△ 44	⊚ 396	O 132		5	4	5	3	5	1.25	1.5	9.4	44
Does not roll	△ 19			⊚ 171	3	3	3	3	4	1.33	1	4	19
Total	105	465	339	219	1122					Total		21.2	100
%	9	41	30	19	99								
company now	5"	3pgs	3g	70%									
competitor x	5"	5pgs	2g	80%									
competitor y	4"	2.5	4g	60%									
plan	5.5"	6pgs	2g	80%									

Main Correlations

⊚ 9 = strong correlation
O 3 = some correlation
△ 1 = possible correlation
Sales points = 1.5, 1.2, or 1

Figure 2.4 Quality Table, Chart A-1, Pencil Example[2][3]

---

2   R. Hasegawa, Y. Maegawa, Aizawa (1983); "Quality/Cost - Technical Deployment Table for New Product Development", Vol. 13, No. 3, pp.92-97, JSQC

3   Refer to Note 2 of the Preface.

Individual product planning

The individual product planning is greatly expanded in QFD by better defining the product. The overall design time is greatly reduced as indicated in Chapter 1.[4]

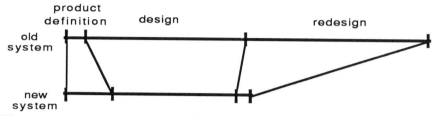

Figure 2.5 Design Time Reductions

It is at the stage of individual product planning that product definition is accomplished. QFD has many tools to help improve this stage. There are five sections to product definition. These include establishing:
  the quality plan
  the cost plan
  the technology plan
  the reliability plan
  the new concept plan

Each of these plans has four parts:
  the customers' demands
  the product function
  quality characteristics
  parts

Each of these has a specific matrix chart and all the charts taken together are called the Matrix of Matrices.

The power of the matrix as a tool is that it is a disciplined way of comparing two series of items. This provides a logical, in-depth look at many of the critical aspects of any product or service. The bulk of this book deals with the construction and use of these charts.

---

4 See page 1-2.

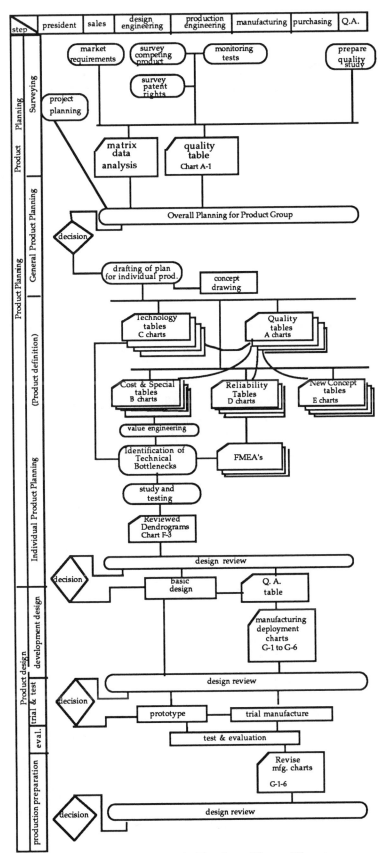

Figure 2.6 Design Flow Chart

In defining the individual product it is looked at from many different perspectives. Some of these perspectives are defined here:

• The QFD Matrix of Matrices uses several matrices in which various product aspects are compared with each other. See Figure 2.2, page 2-6.

• Each chart is a matrix formed by the items on the top and the items to the left. For example, Chart A-1 compares customer demands with quality characteristics. Chart D-2 compares functions with product failure modes. Chart E-4 compares parts with new concepts and so on.

• The filling in of these charts makes it possible to look at the product from many dimensions and thereby have a better understanding of the product and minimize the chance of missing important considerations.

• In flow chart forms this could be portrayed as on the flow chart.

• All company organizations review the tables and charts generated as part of the Matrix of Matrices.

Product design

During the product design phase there are three stages: design development, prototype, and testing and evaluation.

Design development

This stage is the development of the product and the manufacturing process. The quality tables are redone based on the results of the last design review and the manufacturing deployment charts are developed.

The quality tables include Chart A-1, which compares customer demands with quality characteristics; Chart A-2, which compares function with quality characteristics; Chart A-3, which confirms that all negative correlations between one quality characteristic and another have been dealt with, and Chart A-4, which lists all parts (including new parts) and identifies key parts and critical quality characteristics to be controlled in the manufacturing phase. These critical quality characteristics are detailed in Chart B-4.

During this phase the manufacturing deployment is also conducted. Critical quality characteristics are established (G-1), suppliers of parts are determined (G-2), a quality plan is established (G-3), process failure modes are identified (G-4), Process FMEA's (Failure Mode and Effect Analyses) are conducted (G-5), and the full quality control system is mapped out (G-6).

This is followed by trial manufacture, test and evaluation. Process FMEA, QC Process Charts for parts, and assembly and job instruction sheets and standards are revised.

This is followed by final design review and regular manufacturing.

<u>Manufacturing</u>

After beginning manufacturing, only small things change. All major changes are kept for the next model.

Chapter 3

Understanding the Customer

The customer may always be right, but finding out what he really wants is not necessarily an easy task. We will consider three tools in this chapter that will, if not make the task easier, at least give it a higher than normal confidence level. These tools include:

> Matrix Data Analysis
> Structured Customer Surveys
> Analysis and Segmentation of Customer Views

Matrix Data Analysis is one of the Seven New Tools. It makes it possible to map customer demands into market segments. Many things can be segmented in this way. The following chart looks at climate. It is possible on an x and y axis to plot temperature (hot vs. cold) and precipitation (wet vs. dry).

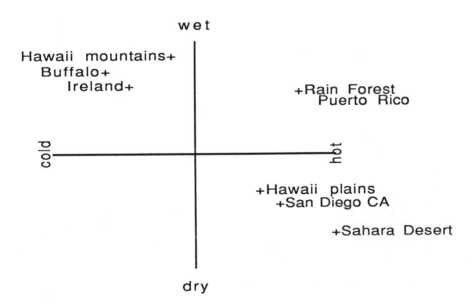

Figure 3.1 Illustration of Matrix Data Analysis using Weather

Some of these examples are obvious. Ireland is perceived as cold and damp. Buffalo is generally quite snowy in the winter as a result of the lake effect snow. The Sahara desert is hot and dry. But consider Hawaii, the Big Island. It has parts that are quite rainy and parts that are quite dry.

When we look at products, we can find a wealth of information through looking at market segmentation. Take for example this perceptual map for pain relievers.

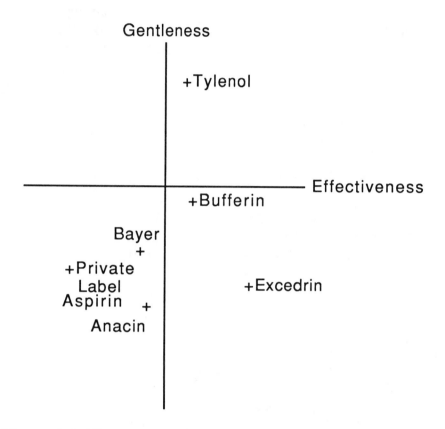

Figure 3.2 Illustration of Matrix Data Analysis Using Pain Relievers

One can further look at the cluster of customer interest on the scales of gentleness and effectiveness. Some people prefer gentle medication as a priority and some prefer effectiveness as the primary consideration. That might be portrayed graphically on the following page.

It is beyond the scope of this text to go into the detailed explanations of market segmentation.[1]   However, it should be clear from these charts that the widespread knowledge of matrix data analysis will be a great help in expanding an organization's understanding of customer preferences.

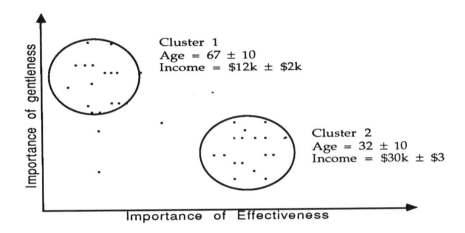

Figure 3.3 Cluster chart on variation in customer preferences for pain relievers

Structured customer surveys

One of the standard kinds of surveys has been to prepare a list of customer demands and conduct focus groups in which you ask customers to rate various items in terms of level of importance with 5 being high importance and 1 being low importance. The next step is to compare various products to see to what extent they meet these requirements, with 5 being very good and 1 being very poor. You might look at hamburgers as an example. (Fig. 3.4)

This seems at first blush a good way to find out what customers want. In fact there has been an increase in the use of surveys by non-marketing people. Design engineers, for example, are going out to ask very specific questions about their product--more specific, in fact, than the marketing people would do. One of the problems of this is that

[1]Thanks is extended to Professor John Hauser of MIT for his help in understanding Matrix Data Analysis.   For more information the reader is directed to one of his texts: *Essentials of New Product Management* by John R. Hauser, Glen L. Urban, and Nikhilesh Dholakia.   Prentice-Hall., Englewood Cliffs, New Jersey 07632. 1987.

customers don't tell you everything. Also it ignores the fact that company specialists know of possibilities that customers may never have considered.

Hamburger survey

Customer Demand	Importance	Brand	Rating
tastes good	1 2 3 ④ 5	x	1 2 ③ 4 5
	.	y	1 2 3 ④ 5
		z	① 2 3 4 5
low in fat	1 2 ③ 4 5	x	1 ② 3 4 5
		y	1 2 ③ 4 5
		z	1 2 3 ④ 5

Figure 3.4 Survey example

Some interesting work has been done by Professor Kano in Japan to look at these possibilities. One of his charts, Figure 3.5, shows the relationship between physically fulfilled conditions and the satisfied feeling of the user.

The arrow in the middle, "one-dimensional quality", represents the cases where the customers tell you what they want, you give it to them and they are happy. Of the three it comes the closest to specifications.

The arrow on the bottom represents the items that are expected. Because they are expected, customers are less likely to tell you about them. They are dissatisfiers if they are missing because they are expected. If they are there they are low on the satisfaction scale because they are expected. "Safety" is an example of this category. If a product is safe, it is expected. If it is unsafe, people are most unhappy. "Paper products in a rest room" are in this category, "expected" and "a dissatisfier" if they are missing.

The arrow at the top represents "exciting quality". These are the items that the producers or service providers develop themselves. The items can be satisfiers but not dissatisfiers. The customers don't know about the items so they can't expect them. They also won't ask for these items in an open ended focus group. These are a product of the talent of the producer or service organization.

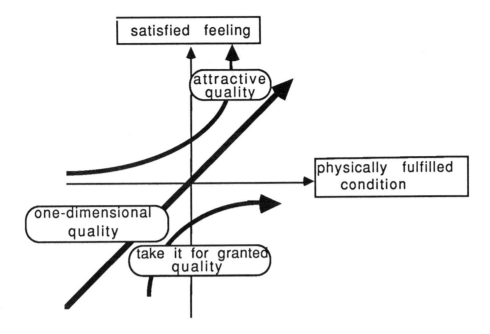

Figure 3.5 Concept chart showing the relation between the physically fulfilled condition and the satisfied feeling of the user.[2]

Dr. W. Edwards Deming has cautioned those who during the last few years have jumped into surveys as if they were a quick fix. The upper and lower arrows on this chart show real limitations to surveys.

Mr. Kano has further developed a style of questionnaire to improve the survey process based on the insights of one-dimensional, expected and exciting quality. They were used in an airline survey.

Some of the categories for the survey of airline customers were the following:
1. Ground hostesses' attitude toward customers
2. Preparation of furnishings on board
3. Meals
4. Comfortable or uncomfortable ride
5. Safety policies
6. Regular flights

---

[2]   Noritaki Kano, Nobuhiro Seraku, Fumio Takahashi, Shinichi Tsuji, (1984) Attractive Quality and Must Be Quality: "Quality", Vol. 14, No. 2, pp.39-48.

Multiple choice questions were developed to help determine whether the item was expected quality, exciting quality or one dimensional quality. A sample follows:

| How do you feel if the ground hostesses have a good attitude toward their customers? | 1. I like it.
2. It is expected to be that way.
3. I do not feel anything.
4. There is no other choice.
5. I don't like it. | How do you feel if the ground hostesses don't have a good attitude toward their customers? | A. I like it.
B. It is expected to be that way.
C. I do not feel anything.
D. There is no other choice.
E. I don't like it. |

Figure 3.6 Sample airline survey from Kano

The answers to these parallel questions are then plotted together on a matrix. The comparison of the answers helps identify whether the particular customer demand is exciting quality, one-dimensional quality or expected quality. The chart follows:

Negative Question Answers

Ground Hostesses' Attitudes toward their customers		I like it	It is expected to be that way	I do not feel anything	There is no other choice	I don't like it	Explanation:
		A	B	C	D	E	C-1 exciting Quality. C-2 not interested C-3 not interested C-4 minus evaluation D-1 exciting Quality D-2 not interested D-3 not interested E-1 one dimensional Quality E-2 expected Quality E-3 expected Quality E-4 no effect
1	I like it			5	4	42	
2	It is expected to be that way			3	6	21	
3	I do not feel anything			3	4	10	
4	There is no other choice			1		1	
5	I don't like it						

Positive Question Answers

Figure 3.7. Survey results, Kano[3]

---

[3]   Kano, same as above.

If one compares the results, they total as follows:

One-dimensional quality	Expected quality	Exciting quality
E-1 42%	E-2 21%	C-1 5%
	E-3 10%	D-1 4%
	31%	9%

Other: Meaningless answers

What this is saying is that people look at the attitude of ground hostesses in different ways. For the largest number of people, 42%, the issue is one-dimensional. If the attitude is good, they are happy; if the attitude is poor, they are unhappy. For a large 31%, a good attitude is expected and for a small number a good attitude represents exciting quality. Recognizing these differences could be important in planning quality.

To review some of the other items taking the largest responses:

Exciting Quality	preparation of furnishings on-board meals
One-Dimensional Quality	ground hostesses' attitude regular flights
Expected Quality	comfortable rides safety policies

Analysis of Customer Words

The final tool is one developed by the author to help sort out, understand and interpret information from customers and to put it in usable forms for the various QFD chart. This tool is also used to suggest other items that, although not mentioned, are explicitly implied.

The information from customers is sorted into the following charts:

	A	B	C	D	E
1	customer words	customer demands	quality characteristics	functions	mechanisms
2					
3					
4					
5					
6					
7					
8					
9					
10					

	F	G	H	I	J
1	new technology	new concepts	product failure modes	parts (sub-systems)	parts failure modes
2					
3					
4					
5					
6					
7					
8					
9					
10					

Figure 3.8   Customer Information Category Charts

These charts are filled in as is practical to begin to separate the customer information into the appropriate categories to be plugged into the matrix of matrices.

Chapter 4

Chart A-1 Quality Table

Chart A-1 maps out in matrix form what the customer wants and how the company will meet that need. It is the most popular and one of the most important of the QFD charts.

Description of the chart

Like most of QFD charts, the Quality Table is a matrix. It has two parts. The left section of the chart compares customer demands with quality characteristics and identifies strong, moderate and possible correlations. The right section of the chart lists on a scale of 1-5 customer demands, company's current performance, competitors' performance, company plan and potential strong and moderate sales points. It combines these weights into an absolute quality weight and a relative quality weight (a percentage).

Purpose of the chart

Chart A-1 lists the customer demands and develops the initial plan of how they will be met based on the current level of performance as compared to competitor's performance. It prioritizes the importance of each customer demand and takes into account potential sales points. It also develops the quality characteristics which are the controllable items, making it possible to meet customer demands. This first chart identifies also the three or four key quality characteristics to work on.

Summary

Inputs: customer demands, quality characteristics, competitors' ratings, company ratings

Outputs: 3 or 4 key quality characteristics, priorities for design, company plans

Background of the chart

The need for improvements in the design system became obvious in Japan in the late 1960's. Deming had introduced the importance of understanding variation starting in June of 1950. By the mid 1960's, it was believed that the tools for understanding and controlling variation should be known by all employees. It also became clear that improvement efforts were being hindered by poor design. The Quality Table Matrix became a key in better definition of product based on customer demands.

How it fits into the design effort

The Quality Table is used during product planning. It is used after general product planning as a basis to begin to define individual products, or to do a major upgrade of existing products.[1]

---

[1] See pages 2-3 and 2-4 for more details of how this chart fits into the design process.

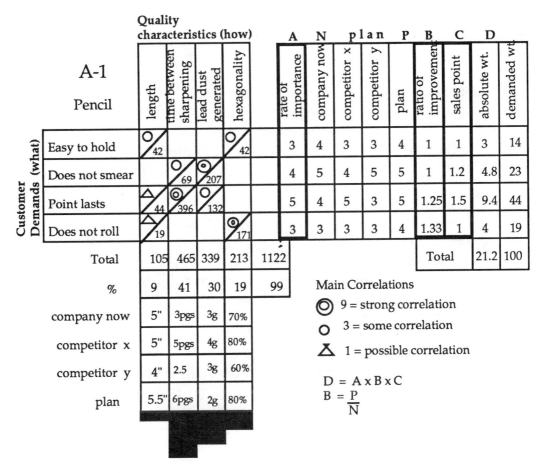

Figure 4.1 Pencil Example Chart A-1

Comments

Rate of importance: the "point lasts" is most important (5); "not smearing" is very important (4)

Competitor comparison: company is behind on "point lasting" (4-5); and also on "smearing" (5-5)

Sales points: "point lasting" will be an excellent sales point; "does not smear", a good sales point

Customer demands priority: "point lasts" is highest (44%)

Quality characteristics: "time between sharpening" is most important (41%)

Target values: length will be increased slightly, 5" to 5.5"; "time between sharpening" will be nearly doubled

Cross checks: all seem consistent except, perhaps, hexagonality when it is compared with "does not roll"

Instructions for filling out Chart A-1, Part 1

1. List the customer demands in column 1. These customer demands were derived using the three tools of Matrix Data Analysis, Structured Customer Surveys, and Analysis and Segmentation of Customer Views.[2] Additional sources of information include:

> needs as expressed in trade journals
> warranty claims or customer complaints
> from company
> analysis of failures (e.g., FMEA charts)
> face to face interviews, sometimes over a beverage
>   (known as the Jack Daniels Method)
> results from letting customers try out your equipment
> or service

Each customer demand should be defined and fed back to the customer to make sure the definition is correct. This process of getting information and feeding it back and forth from customer to supplier has been described as a "game of catch" by Masaki Imai.[3]

Customer demands should be in customer language (but understood easily by supplier employees), describe customer values, be precise, e.g., verb plus modifier easy to use or noun plus adjective e.g., high reliability, low cost. There should be no numbers since these are too limiting. They should be positive if possible.

Take all of this language data and arrange it using the Affinity Diagram. Then arrange and fill in missing information using the Tree Diagram.[4] Fill in the chart using the first 3 levels of the Tree Diagram. (Note: On large lists of 100 or so items, initially it is advisable to do a chart at two levels (app. 30 items) and then redo the chart at three levels with the priority items.)

---

[2]   See Chapter 3 for explanation of these tools

[3]   See Appendix A.

[4]   See Appendix A, Part 3.

2. List the rate of importance of each demanded item. Use a scale of 1 to 5, with 5 being most important and 1 being of relatively low importance. Some of this information is available through customer surveys. Other information is available through knowledgeable sales and marketing professionals. Some information may have to be guessed at until it is possible to verify it with customers. (The Saaty system of ranking is a useful substitute when you cannot survey customers.)

3. Company now: list where the company is today on each customer demand on a scale of 1 to 5, with 5 being very good and 1 being very poor. This item is subject to the same procedures described above in item 2.

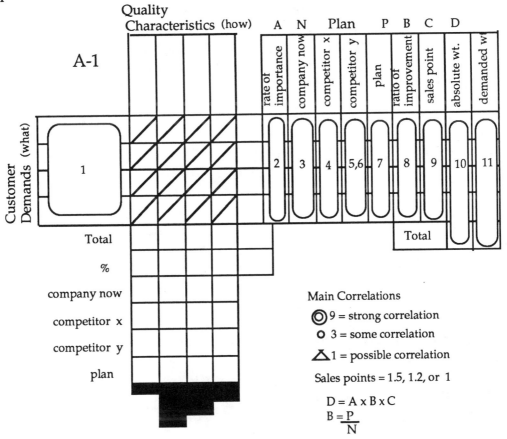

Figure 4.2 Instructions for Chart A-1, Part 1

4. List how competitor a is doing in regard to each customer demand on a scale of 1 to 5. Some testing may be required here. Also some trade magazines and others do comparative reporting.

5. List how <u>competitor b</u> is doing on the customer demands.

6. List how <u>competitor c</u> is doing on customer demands. In some cases it may make sense to look at greater or fewer numbers of customers. If you are sharing this chart with a customer you may be unwilling to share competitor information with him.

7. <u>Company plan</u> is listed for each customer demand. This is determined by looking at where the company is today in relation to the competitors and in relation to the customer's rate of importance. It also takes into account the company's strategic plan, policy deployment,[5] or other planning documents. It is also important to consider what the competitor is currently working on in developing the plan.

8. Identify <u>improvement ratio</u> by dividing where the company plans to be (column 7) by where the company is today (column 3).

9. List the level of <u>sales point</u> with a 1.5, for a strong sales point; a 1.2, for a lesser sales point; and a 1.0, for items which are not sales points. Akao suggests a maximum of three major sales points to avoid the temptation of making everything a sales point.

10. Calculate the <u>absolute quality weight</u> by multiplying the rate of importance (column 2) times the rate of improvement (column 8) times the sales point (column 9), i.e., (2)(8)(9) = (10.)

11. Calculate the <u>demanded quality weight</u> by converting the absolute quality weight to a percentage, i.e., divide the total of column 10 into each item to get the percentage of each item.

The purpose of this exercise is then achieved by picking the top 3 or 4 customer demands to work on.

---

5   Policy Deployment is the Japanese approach to strategic planning which focuses on systems rather than individuals and includes all individuals in the organization in the improvement effort. By having each individual take responsibility for planning, it has a high motivational effect.

Instructions for Chart A - 1, Part 2

12. Generate the absolute quality characteristics for each of the customer demands. These are the items that are controlled to assure that customer demands are met. They are grouped by the affinity method and then by the tree diagram with missing items filled in. Then the first three levels are listed on the chart. [6] (In the case of 75-100 items first use two levels and then redo selection priority items and expand to three levels.)

Quality characteristics should indicate what is measured or controlled. They should not include parts or names of tests. If you ask what you test for you will get some ideas for quality characteristics.

13. Fill in the correlations between the customer demands and the quality characteristics using the double circle, or 9, for strong correlation; the circle, or 3, for some correlation; and the triangle, or 1, for possible correlation. Multiply each factor 9, 3, 1 times the absolute weight for that column and put the total in the box under the corresponding symbol.

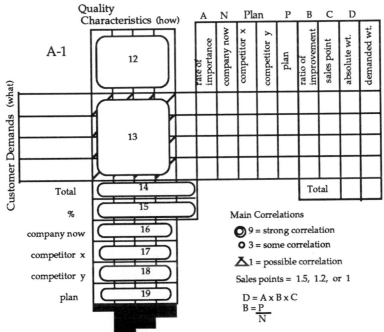

Figure 4.3 Instructions or Chart A-1, Part 2

---

6   See Appendix A, parts 1 and 3 for an explanation of how to fill out the affinity and tree diagrams.

14. Total each column.

15. Convert each item from row 14 to a percentage, i.e., add the numbers across in row 14 and divide the total into each number.

16. List the current value for each quality characteristic that is measurable.

17. List the values for competitor a for each quality characteristic.

18. List the values for competitor b for each quality characteristic.

19. List the target value for each quality characteristic based on a review of each competitor.

Analysis: The top three or four quality characteristics should be compared with the top three or four customer demands. The integration of these two serves as a basis to select items to work on.

Based on this exercise it is possible to select the key quality characteristics to work on. Some companies use this as a priority list for design engineers.[7]

---

[7]   Dave Taylor of Cirtek reported this practice at a case review meeting at Ford World Headquarters in March of 1987.

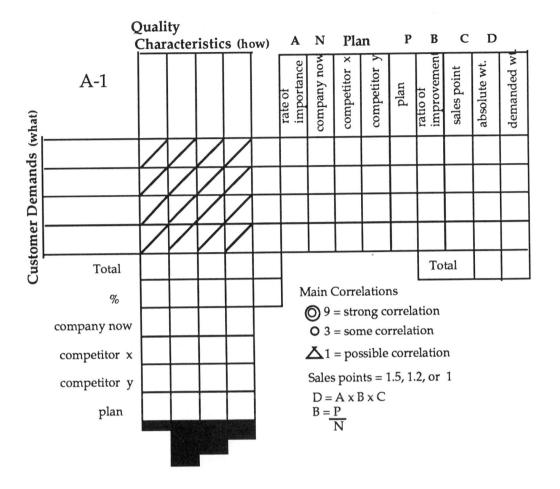

Figure 4.4 Practice Chart for A-1, Part 1

Helpful hints and further comments on Chart A-1

1. A list of definitions should be developed for customer demands and quality characteristics. Much time is wasted in disagreements over correlations because of different usages of terms.

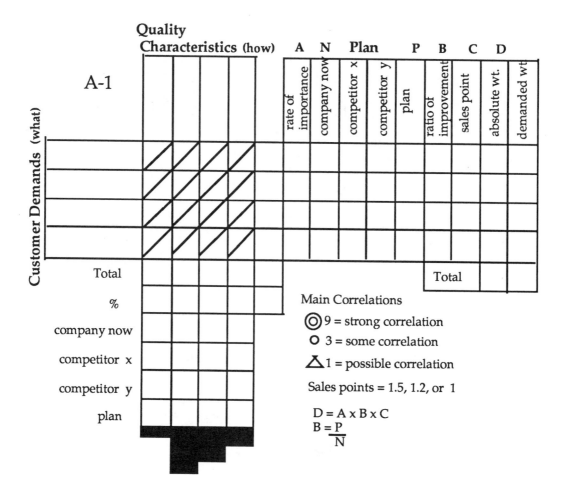

Figure 4.5 Practice Chart A-1, Part 2

2. Some instructors leave out the "sales point" part of Chart A-1. This may lead to misleading results. As indicated in Chapter 3 (in Kano Three Arrow Treatment of customer demands), expected quality and exciting quality are often not shared by customers. Leaving out the sales point will lead to a lack of priority for these key items.

Chapter 5

Chart A-2   Quality Characteristics/ Functions

Chart A-2 compares product or service functions with the quality characteristics.

Description of the chart

Chart A-2 is a matrix which has the quality characteristics on the top and the functions on the left side. The correlations are indicated by a double circle, or 9, for strong correlation; a circle, or 3, for some correlation; and a triangle, or 1, for possible correlation.

Purpose of the chart

The purpose of the chart is to identify functions of the product that might not be known to the customer. The chart makes it possible to present the functions in a logical format to make sure that none are missed. The chart identifies functions for which there are not yet any quality characteristics and quality characteristics for which there is no function, and thereby helps assist the initial product planning.

Summary

Inputs: functions and quality characteristics

Outputs: better definition of functions and quality characteristics

Background of the chart

After some experience doing Chart A-1, it became clear that there were many critical items that were not known to the customers. For the sake of completeness Chart A-2 was added. It made it possible to take a fresh look at the product or service as seen by the most experienced people at the producer.

How it fits into the design effort

Chart A-2 is used in the product planning stage under the category of individual product planning.

Special Caution: Voice of the engineer and voice of the customer.

This is a very important chart because it focuses on the voice of the engineer. Some companies who only use Chart A-1 mix the voice of the customer and the voice of the engineer in one chart. This has lead to some confusion. It is better to put the voice of consumer in Chart A-1 and the voice of the engineer in Chart A-2.

When your product is prepared for an OEM customer then this distinction is more difficult. It is the author's recommendation to put functions and technical issues in Chart A-2 and more general considerations like ease of assembly in Chart A-1. If your only customer is an OEM engineer you may not have many items for Chart A-1. In this case it is important to prioritize the functions in A-2. The Saaty method is recommended.[1]

---

[1] Saaty, Thomas L., Decision Making, The Analytic Hierarchy Process (Pittsburgh, PA: University of Pittsburgh), 1988. Also Saaty, Thomas L., Decision Making for Leaders (Pittsburgh, PA: University of Pittsburgh), 1988.

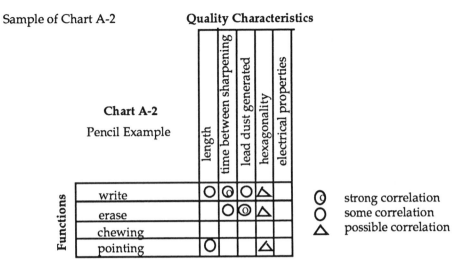

Figure 5.1 Pencil example, Chart A-2

Comments

1. In reviewing the correlations there are strong correlations for function of writing and erasing.

2. In regard to pointing there are some correlations, but not strong ones. Pointing may not be appropriate. Some have suggested adding a bulb to the pencil for pointing purposes.

3. There are no correlations for chewing. Chewing as a function should be deleted as not appropriate or controlled by adding some quality characteristics. Some students have suggested flavored pencils with matching colors, e.g., red for cherry, yellow for lemon. Toxicity may be an appropriate quality characteristic.

4. There are no correlations of the quality characteristic electrical properties with functions -- so it should be deleted or an appropriate function added, e.g. shining light.

Instructions for filling out Chart A-2

1. Bring down all the quality characteristics from
Chart A-1.

2. Bring together the most knowledgeable people and
brainstorm product or service functions. Functions are a
statement of what the product or service does. Do an affinity
chart of the product functions and then do a tree diagram
filling in the missing functions and subsystems.[1]

3. Do a correlation of quality characteristics as they relate to
functions using a double circle, or 9, for strong correlation; a
single circle, or 3, for some correlation; and a triangle, or 1, for
possible correlation.

Review the chart. If there are quality characteristics with
no correlation to functions, check to see if the quality
characteristic should be eliminated or if some function or
subfunction has been left out. If there are functions with no
correlations to quality characteristics, add the appropriate
quality characteristic(s).

---

[1]Those who are familiar with value engineering may use the
FAST diagram to generate the function tree. See other notes
on page 5-6.

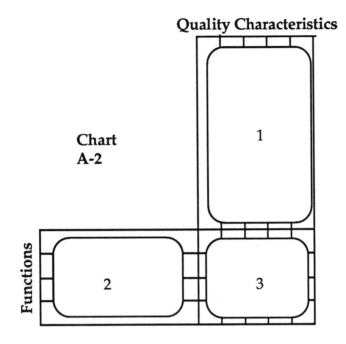

Figure 5.2 Instructions Chart A-2

Quality Characteristics

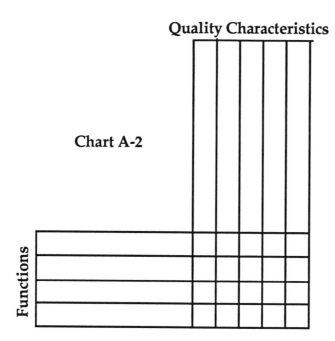

Chart A-2

Figure 5.3 Practice Chart A-2

<u>Suggestions</u>

There has been a lot of research done on function statements by value engineering specialists. One might consider using some of their principles for enhancing the statements of function.

1. Function should be described by a verb and a noun.

2. Avoid passive or indirect verbs such as provides, supplies, gives, furnishes.

3. Avoid goal-like words or phrases such as improve, maximize, minimize.

4. Keep similar levels of abstraction, e.g., in pencil do not mix items like wood, graphite and eraser, with pigment, solvent and carrier.[1]

5. The FAST system is helpful in grouping functions and subfunctions.

---

[1] These ideas were shared by Larry Shillito of Kodak at the August 1987 course and also appear in his chapter on value engineering in the industrial engineering handbook.

Chapter 6

Chart A-3   Quality Characteristics/ Quality Characteristics

Chart A-3 compares quality characteristics against themselves.

Description of the chart

Chart A-3 is a matrix that has quality characteristics on the top and quality characteristics on the side. The double circle represents strong positive correlation. The single circle represents some positive correlation. The "#" represents strong negative correlation and the "x" represents some negative correlation.

Purpose of the chart

The purpose of the chart is to find out which quality characteristics interact with others. This is important to know because designers need to know that if they change one item they will be changing another item either positively or negatively. For example, in a car sun roof, the "ease of opening" may have a negative correlation with "does not leak". This chart would highlight that negative correlation with a "#".

Summary

Inputs: quality characteristics

Outputs: potential opportunities and problems arising out of correlations of quality characteristics with each other.

Background of the chart

This chart was developed because one of the major problems with design is not what is not known; it is interactions that are forgotten. This chart helps the design engineer systematically consider correlations of quality characteristics and as a result, not forget things. It is also helpful when two engineers are working on two different components so they know who to notify in case of changes.

How it fits into the design effort

This is a chart that goes to the engineers who are designing the product to alert them to interrelations before hand. This chart may also be used to determine some of the items that should be optimized using the design of experiments.[1]

---

[1] See Chapter 26, page 7 regarding Taguchi and factor analysis.

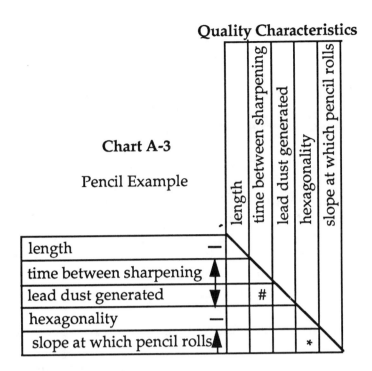

Figure 6.1 Pencil example, Chart A-3

1. There is a strong correlation between time between sharpening and lead dust generated. The correlation is negative because as the lead dust generated increases, the time between sharpening is shortened.

2. This chart presents a real opportunity for use of fractional factorial as popularized by Taguchi, and optimization of product design.

In the case of lead dust generated there are some tradeoffs. It is the generation of lead dust that enables lead to adhere to existing surface, making a line. Too much lead dust can result in a problem of smearing. Too little lead dust can result in a faint line which is hard to read. Taguchi's methods help delineate the right amount of lead dust to get the best results at the lowest cost and with the easiest-to-control manufacturing standards.

*   This chart can also indicate opportunities for planned experimentation (symbols T for Taguchi or BHH Box Hunter, Hunter, or DOE). There is an optimal value which combines the most comfort to hold and the greatest slope at which it will not roll. Also see page 6-6 for description of use of arrows.

Instructions for filling out Chart A-3

1. Bring down the quality characteristics.

2. Bring down the quality characteristics.

3. Identify the correlations of each quality characteristic with each other. Show strong positive correlation with a double circle; show some positive correlation with a circle. Show strong negative correlation with a "#"; show some negative correlation with an "x". Make a note of each correlation and use procedures to assure that they are taken into account by design engineers.

Note: Some companies are also using a "T" to indicate correlations where design of experiments based on Taguchi, Box and Hunter or some other format will be used to optimize the process.[2]

---

[2]   As presented by Joseph Meyers of Sheller Globe, Keokuk, Iowa, at the case studies presentation in March of 1987 at Ford World Headquarters.

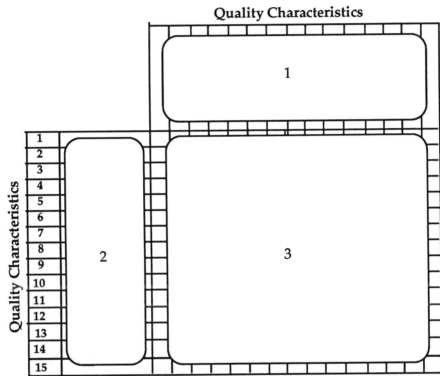

Figure 6.2 Instructions Chart A-3

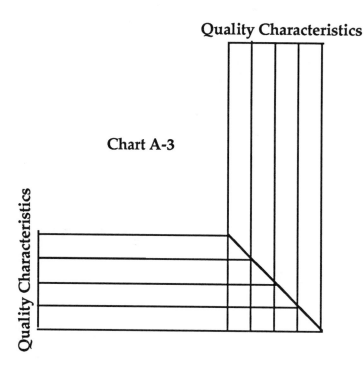

Figure 6.3 Practice Chart A-3

Suggestions

1. Sometimes there is confusion about whether to consider a correlation as positive or negative. Ford Light Truck ran into this problem in its study to improve tire wear on the Ranger. Items like caster and camber were being considered in some cases positive and in others negative. The idea of arrows was developed to indicate which direction was good. This helped sort out negative from positive correlations. A dash can also be used to indicate a specific preferred value.

Time between sharpening should be increased; lead dust generated should be decreased.

Chapter 7

Chart A-4   Quality Characteristics/Parts

Chart A - 4 is a matrix which examines the correlations between the quality characteristics and the second level of detail or parts of the product or service.[1]

Description of the chart

Chart A-4 is a matrix bounded on the top by the most critical quality characteristics and on the left by the parts. The correlations are identified in the matrix by a double circle for strong correlations, by a circle in the case of some correlation, and by a triangle in the case of possible correlation.

Purpose of the chart

The purpose of the chart is to identify which parts are most related to the three or four critical quality characteristics which are being highlighted for breakthrough. Unlike Charts A-2 and A-3 only the critical quality characteristics appear on the top of the matrix.

Summary

Inputs: parts and critical quality characteristics

Outputs: critical parts to be controlled and optimized

---

[1]When you conduct a QFD study there is the product or service being designed. There is the first level of detail which is most often referred to as mechanism and information is put on the column C charts. There is the second level of detail which is often called parts and this information is placed in Chart A-4. For a more detailed explanation see pgs. 2-4 and 2-5.

Background of the chart

This was one of the earliest charts to be developed. It was recognized that critical parts had to be identified and controlled. By 1975, this chart was becoming popular in Japan as a way to assist this control.

Its role in design

This chart is actually used twice in design. It is used initially in product planning of an individual part. It is later used after new concept selection and optimization because of new parts that are introduced and/or deleted. It is a chart also subject to modification after prototype testing.

Sample of Chart A-4

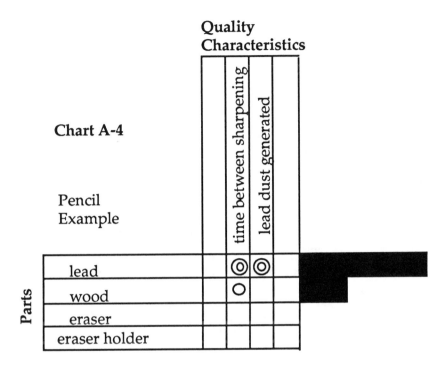

Figure 7.1 Pencil example Chart A-4

1. Lead is the item to be controlled because it has a strong correlation with time between sharpening and lead dust generated.

2. The wood is of some significance because it can affect lead breakage.

3. In service examples use people and procedures instead of parts. In chemical or process industries use raw materials or processes instead of parts.

<u>Instructions for filling out Chart A-4</u>

1. Bring down the three or four key quality characteristics as identified in Chart A-1.

2. Have the most knowledgeable people develop a list of parts (or second level of detail). Categorize them using the affinity and tree diagrams.

3. Identify the correlations between the quality characteristics and parts using a double circle for a strong correlation, a circle for some correlation and a triangle for possible correlation.

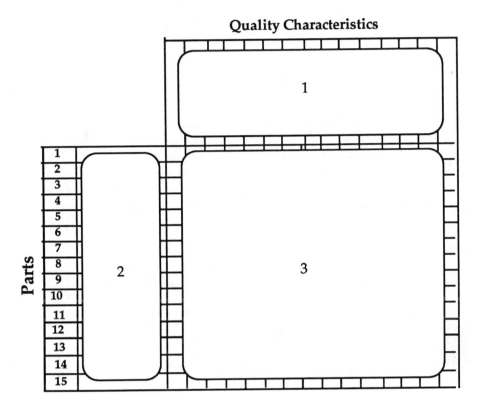

Figure 7.2 Instructions Chart A-4

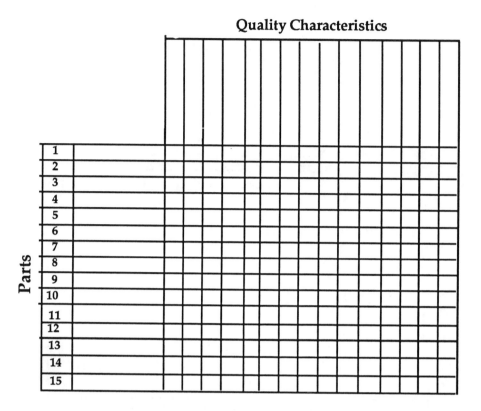

Figure 7.3 Practice Chart A-4

<u>Suggestions</u>

1. Although in its development and recommended usage it comes later, it is probably easier to develop first level of detail (or mechanisms) first and then develop the second level of detail (or parts).

See Chart C-1, Chapter 12.

Chapter 8

Chart B-1   Functions/Customer Demands

Chart B-1 is a matrix which examines the correlations between functions and customer demands and determines the relative value of each of the functions from the perspective of the customer.

Description of the chart

Chart B-1 is a matrix bounded on the top by the product or service functions and on the left by the customer demands. The correlations are identified in the matrix by the double circle, or 9, for strong correlation; the circle, or 3, for some correlation; and the triangle, or 1, for possible correlation. The columns are added vertically and converted to percentages to identify the relative value of each function. This percentage is multiplied by the target cost to give the targeted cost for each function. This targeted cost is compared to the actual cost to identify functions for cost reduction by value engineering.

The purpose of the chart

The purpose of the chart is to identify functions to be the target of cost reduction by identifying which ones have an actual cost which exceeds the expected cost.

Summary

Inputs: functions, customer demands, target cost

Outputs: functions targeted for cost reduction

Background of the chart

This was one of the earliest of the charts, coming into existence around 1975. The earlier purpose was to challenge the validity of the customer demands to see if there were some latent demands that had not been verbalized. By the middle 1980's the focus shifted with the introduction of cost deployment as a facet of QFD.[1 & 2]

Its role in design

Chart B-1 is used to identify some of the areas of opportunity for breakthrough especially from the cost reduction standpoint. Oftentimes customers ask for cost reductions across the board. Suppliers respond by trying to reduce everything by a certain percentage or by picking large number items. This chart presents another alternative for achieving cost reduction.

---

[1]   See footnote 1 on page 2-8.
[& 2]   Yoji Akao (1987) Quality Function Deployment JSA.

Example of Chart B-1

Functions

Chart B-1 Pencil example	demanded weight	write	erase	chewing	pointing	
easy to hold	14	O / 42	O / 42		Δ / 14	
does not smear	23		◎ / 207	Δ / 23		
point lasts	44	◉ / 396	Δ / 44		Δ / 44	
does not roll	19	Δ / 19			Δ / 19	
column wt.		457	293	23	77	850
function wt.		54%	34%	3%	9%	
function target cost		6.5¢	4¢	.4¢	1¢	12¢
function actual cost		4¢	4¢	3¢	2¢	13¢

Customer Demands

Figure 8.1 Pencil example, Chart B-1

Instructions for filling out Chart B-1

1. List the functions from Chart A-2.

2. List the customer demands from Chart A-1.

3. Plot the correlations between customer demands and functions using a double circle, or 9, for strong correlation; a single circle, or 3, for some correlation; and a triangle, or 1, for possible correlation.

   Examine the functions for which there are no customer demands and consider whether some customer demands have been overlooked or whether functions have been added unnecessarily.

   Examine the customer demands with no function and consider whether some functions or subfunctions have been omitted.

4. Total the values of the functions.

5 Convert the absolute function numbers to percentages by dividing the total of row 4 into each individual item.

6. Multiply the function weight (5) times the target value from Chart B-2 to get the expected function cost.

7. Fill in the actual function costs by considering the percentage of weights that accomplish this function.

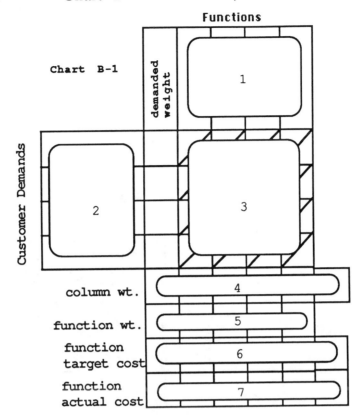

Figure 8.2 Instructions Chart B-1

Suggestions

1. The function target cost and function actual cost are compared in what value analysts call the cost/value analysis. It is usually portrayed thus:

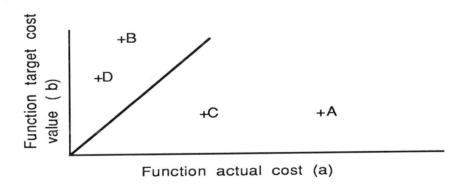

Figure 8.3 Example of Value Analysis Chart

When a > b then it is a target for cost reduction, e.g., in chart items C and A.

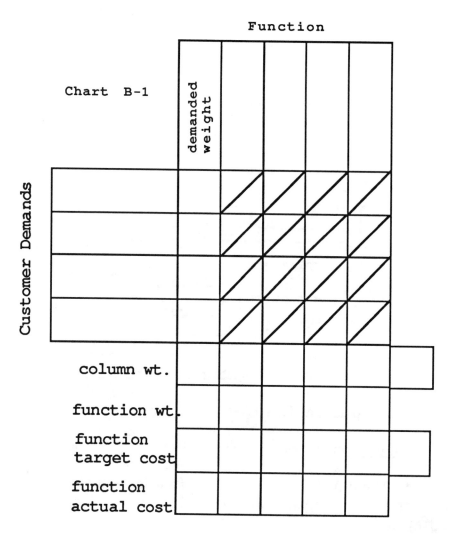

Figure 8.4 Practice Chart B-1

    2. The value index and cost index in the absence of QFD were determined by a pacing system in which each item was compared against each other. QFD seems to be an improvement by adding in some objective criteria.

    3. FOM (Figures of Merit) or value index can be used to determine costs.[3]

---

[3]   D.J. Demarle, "The Nature and Measurement of Value".
Proceedings, 23rd Annual AIIE Conference, May 1972, pp. 507-512.

Chapter 9

Chart B-2 Cost Deployment Main Chart

Chart B-2 is a table which compares the company with its competitors on issues such as selling price, market share and target manufacturing cost.

Description of the chart

Chart B-2 identifies market price, sales volume, market share and targeted manufacturing cost as they relate to the current products, the competitor's product and the plan for future product.

Summary

Inputs: market price, sales volume, market share, current manufacturing cost and competitor information for the same

Outputs: targeted manufacturing cost for the new product

Background of the chart

Cost deployment as it relates to QFD is relatively new, starting around 1985. It is a detailed weighting system and will probably go through several revisions before it becomes more widely established. One of the difficulties is that at least in the U. S., current accounting systems do not capture much of the information needed for cost accounting as it is used in QFD.

Its role in the design process

Cost deployment is used early in the individual product development to identify targets for cost reduction through value engineering. It is more easy to use on major product upgrades than in brand new products.

Example

Chart B-2

Pencil Example	Company	Competitor x	Competitor y	plan
Market price	15¢	18¢	14¢	16¢
Sales volume	4M	3M	8M	5M
Market share	16%	12%	32%	20%
Profit[1]	2¢	3¢	2¢	4¢
Cost [1]	13¢	15¢	12¢	12¢
				Target

Figure 9.1 Pencil example Chart B-2

1. Competitor Y is the high volume, low cost pencil producer with 2¢ profit per pencil.

2. Competitor X is the quality pencil maker with 3¢ profit.

3. The plan is to become the 4¢ high profit pencil maker through a slight increase in price and better cost controls.[1]

---

[1] Thomas Register and tear down of competitors' product provides some guides to their cost and profit.

Instructions for Chart B-2

1. List the selling price for current product, competitors' products, and the planned selling price for the new product.

2. List the sales volume for the current product, the competitors' products and the plan for the new product.

3. List the market share for the existing product, for the competitors' products and the plan for the new product.

4. List the profit for the existing product, for the competitors' products and the plan for the new product.

5. List the manufacturing cost for the existing product, the competitors' products and the targeted manufacturing cost for the new product.

	company	comp a	comp b	plan
market price	1			
sales volume	2			
market share	3			
profit	4			
target cost	5			

Figure 9.2 Instructions Chart B-2

Practice Chart B-2 Cost Deployment

	company	comp a	comp b	plan
market price				
sales volume				
market share				
profit				
target cost				

Figure 9.3 Practice Chart B-2

<u>Suggestions</u>

Selection of target selling price varies considerably from industry to industry. Also of concern here is where to include items like advertising and teaching. For the time being, for most organizations target cost is established by a specific organization and reported without explanation. QFD provides a rational way of reaching those target costs.

Chapter   10

Chart B-3   Quality Characteristics Detail/ Breakthrough   Targets

Chart B-3 identifies the fourth level of detail of the three or four key quality characteristics and identifies the breakthrough targets.

Description of the chart

Like Chart B-2, Chart B-3 is more of a table than a chart. It lists the three or four critical quality characteristics identified in Chart A-1, identifies the major factors of each one, the current values and the target values. Some renditions also indicate the level of difficulty of achieving the targeted breakthrough.

Purpose of the chart

Sometimes in design it seems that everything is important. This chart focuses attention on the critical breakthroughs that are required to have a world class product or service.

Summary

Inputs: quality characteristics at the third and fourth level of detail

Outputs: targeted areas for breakthrough

Background of the chart

The chart is relatively new, used first in the early 1980's. It is seen in different formats in different companies due to the variety of ways that companies establish their breakthrough targets, and due to the various weighting systems to measure degree of difficulty.

Role in the design process

This chart plays a central role in the design process. It is the central agenda for critical breakthroughs. It is the focus of the early stages of the design of individual products.

Quality Characteristics

3rd level   4th level

	factors	present value	target value	degree of difficulty	project #
time between sharpening	wood hardness	20 psi to break	20 psi to break	1	101
	lead hardness	#2	#2		
	lead com-position	traditional	lead polymers	3	102
	darkness of line	20 color spectrom.	30 color spectrom.	2	103
lead dust generated	size of dust	10 microns	8 microns	2	104
	amount of dust	10 part./ line	6 part./ line	3	105

Figure 10.1 Pencil example Chart B-3

Comments

1. The most difficult items to be accomplished will be Project 102, which will change chemistry of lead using long polymers, and Project 105, which will reduce the number of particles by making the lead more moist.

2. Projects 103 and 104 are difficult, but the technology exists.

3. Project 101 has already been accomplished, and in fact pencils in the past were made stronger.

Instructions for filling out Chart B-3

1. List the three or four key quality characteristics that were identified in Chart A-1.

Note: Although these will probably be the items with the highest number, if one or two of these have already been optimized, there may be a business judgment to take the one or two with the next highest number.

2. List the major categories of each of the level three items.

3. List the current values of the level four items.

4. List stretch goals for each of the items.

5. Identify the degree of difficulty. If there is a current system in place, use that. If not, use a scale of 1-5 with 1 being difficult and 5 being most difficult.

6. List the project numbers corresponding to each item.

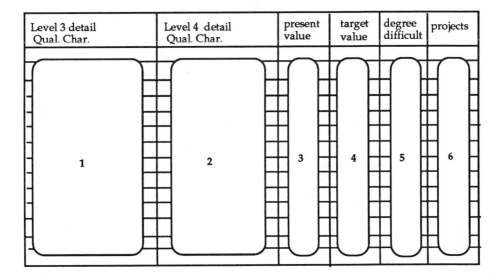

Figure 10.2 Instructions Chart B-3

Level 3 detail Qual. Char.	Level 4 detail Qual. Char.	present value	target value	degree difficult	projects

Figure 10.3 Practice Chart B-3

Suggestions

1. In identifying the level four detail it is helpful to conduct a factor analysis. The fractional factorial made popular by Taguchi may be helpful if there are not a lot of interactions.

2. On degree of difficulty, some companies use a Code 1 if they have done it, Code 2 if they have needed technology but have not implemented it, and a Code 3 if they have no idea how it will be accomplished.

Chapter 11

Chart B-4   Quality Characteristics Plan/ Critical Parts

Chart B-4 identifies the critical parts for function or safety of the product or service and begins to detail function, quality characteristics, target values and specifications.

Description of the chart

Chart B-4, like most of the other charts in column B, is really a table. It looks only at the parts which have a strong correlation with the selected quality characteristics as identified in Chart A-4. It identifies many critical items about each part: its function, its critical quality characteristics, the target value, and the variation as measured by the Cpk factor. The current cost of making the product as well as additional items of interest such as physical weight are optional.

Purpose of the chart

Chart B-4 begins to identify how the quality and cost of critical parts will be controlled.

Summary

Input: parts, critical quality characteristics, specifications

Outputs: critical control items for critical parts

Background of the chart

This is one of the earliest of the QFD charts to be developed in the mid-1970's. At that time the parts critical for function had an "A" with a circle around it and those critical for safety had an "S" with a circle around it. Each of the parts so designated were subjects of value engineering studies.

Use in design

This chart is valuable in design in that it spells out the critical parameters of the critical parts. It is used initially to identify existing conditions in detail. It is later revised as a result of engineering breakthroughs in new product design. In this way Chart B-4 becomes a real benchmark of progress.

	functions	quality characteristics	specs	cpk	wt. grams *	cost *
lead	make mark	darkness of line	8 color spectrometer			
		width of line	8 microns			
	no smear	adhesion of lead	ooo ooo			
		moisture of lead	ooo			
body	hold lead	tolerance to lead	ooo			
	protect lead	tolerance to lead	ooo			
	does not break	resistance to force	ooo			

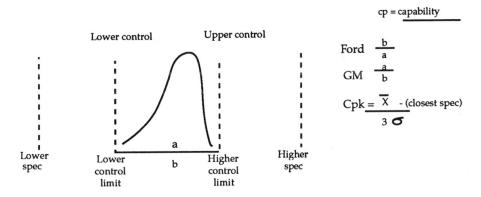

cp = capability

Ford $\dfrac{b}{a}$

GM $\dfrac{a}{b}$

$Cpk = \dfrac{\overline{X} - (\text{closest spec})}{3\sigma}$

*   These columns are optional. They are
used if the company has a special focus
on weight and cost. They could also be
replaced by other company priorities.

Figure 11.1 Pencil example, Chart B-4

Instructions for filling out Chart B-4

1. List the critical parts from Chart A-4, i.e., the ones that had the strong correlations with the quality characteristics.

2. List the functions of the critical parts.

3. List the quality characteristics of the critical parts.

4. List the target value of the the quality characteristics of the critical parts.

5. List the current capability as measured by the Cp index of the critical parts in meeting the target values. The Cp index is measured differently by different companies. The most frequent formula is the variation 6 sigma divided by the tolerance. In the chart below this is indicated by a/b.

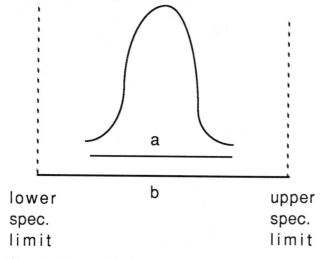

lower
spec.
limit

upper
spec.
limit

Illustration 11.1

6. List the weight in grams of the part.

7. List the current manufacturing cost of the part.

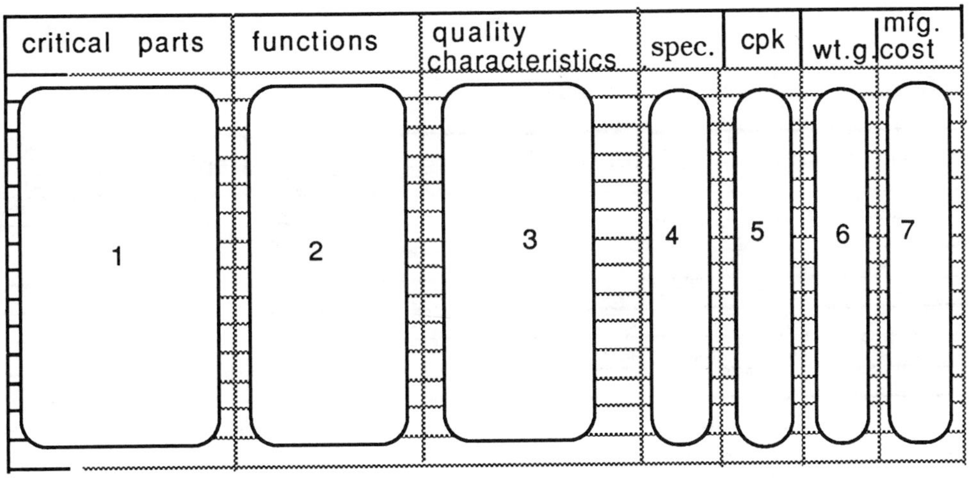

critical parts	functions	quality characteristics	spec.	cpk	wt.g	mfg. cost
1	2	3	4	5	6	7

Figure 11.2   Instructions Chart B-4

critical parts	functions	quality characteristics	spec.	cpk	wt.g	mfg. cost

Figure 11.3 Practice Chart B-4

Chapter 12

Chart C-1   Mechanisms/New Technology

Chart C-1 examines which new technologies may be useful in designing the product and what new product opportunities exist as a result of new technology.

Description of the chart

The chart is a matrix which lists on the top the first level of detail (or mechanism) of the product or service being studied by QFD.[1] The left side of the matrix contains an organized list of new technologies, be they product, raw material, service or process. The matrix shows strong correlations with a double circle, some correlation with a single circle and possible correlation with a triangle.

Purpose of the chart

The purpose of the chart is to identify new technologies which should be considered in developing the new product and to suggest basic new directions for the product based on new technology.

Summary

Inputs: mechanism and new technology

Outputs: new opportunities

---

[1] See Chapter 2, pages 2-3 and 2-4 for an explanation of levels of detail as they relate to the term mechanism in a QFD study.

Background of the chart

The chart became included in the QFD literature around 1985. It is a limited but useful look at new technology. The opportunity for considering new ideas will also be considered in column E which looks at new concepts, and in Chart F-2 which reports on the consideration of new design ideas in the format of the Reviewed Dendrogram.

Use in design

Chart C-1 has an important role to play in the early stages of designing a new product or service. Sometimes opportunities in design are missed because they are not considered early enough in the design process. This chart provides, more than others, the opportunity to consider creatively tying new technology to the various mechanisms. This particular chart has significantly helped the Japanese in developing new patents.

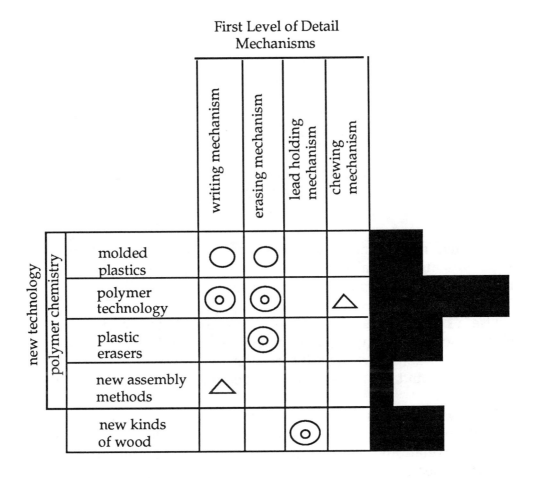

Figure 12.1 Pencil example Chart C-1

1. Polymer technology shows promise for better writing and erasing.

2. Plastics technology shows promise for holding mechanism and eraser composition.

3. No strong correlations for chewing or pointing mechanisms indicated that research and development departments should be alert for new developments here.

Instructions on filling out Chart C-1

1.   Brainstorm all the mechanisms (1st level of detail as explained above). Do an affinity diagram and a tree diagram to the 3rd level.[2]

2.   Brainstorm the new technologies. Use vendors, trade magazines and central engineering as sources. Do an affinity diagram and tree diagram to the third level.

3.   Use a double circle to indicate strong correlation; a circle to indicate some correlation; and a triangle to indicate possible correlation. Consider what the results mean for new product development and for research and development.

4.   Review the results, considering both correlations and lack of correlations. Indicators of need mean more development-- strong correlations lead to new product development; no correlations lead to new agenda for R & D.

---

[2]   See Appendix A, Chapters 1 and 3.

First Level of Detail

Mechanisms

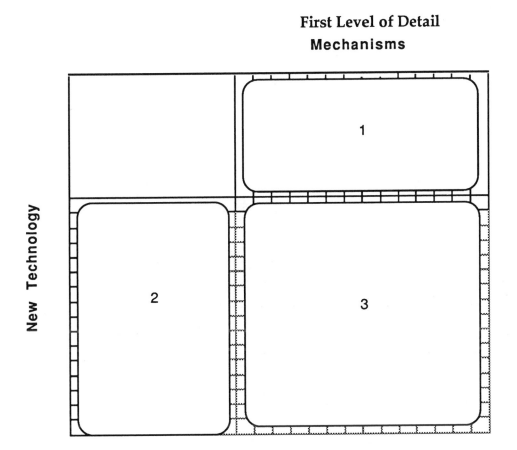

Figure 12.2 Instructions Chart C-1

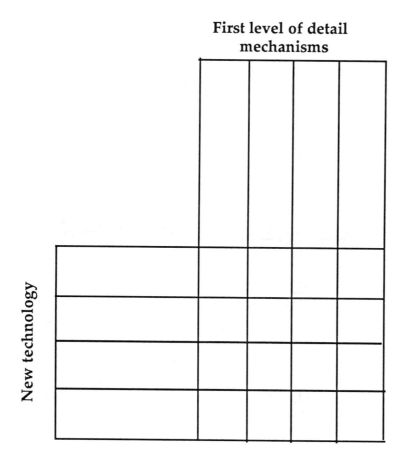

Figure 12.3   Practice Chart C-1

Suggestions

1. This chart can help build bridges between the design engineers, who are sometimes accused of jumping to conclusions too quickly or always using their favorite technology, and research scientists who are sometimes accused of staying in their ivory towers.

Chapter 13

Chart C-2   Mechanisms/Functions

Chart C-2 shows how the mechanisms relate to the function and determines the relative cost value of each mechanism.

<u>Description of the chart</u>

Chart C-2 is a matrix. On the top are the mechanisms which were first listed in Chart C-1. On the left are the functions which were first listed in Chart A-2. The strong correlations are identified with a double circle, or a 9. The instances of some correlation are indicated with a circle, or a 3. The instances of possible correlation are indicated with a triangle, or 1. The bottom row of the chart indicates the expected cost to manufacture each mechanism.

<u>Purpose of the chart</u>

The purpose of the chart is to identify which mechanisms most relate to the key functions. It also makes it possible to identify mechanisms for cost reduction based on their actual cost as compared to the expected cost.

<u>Summary</u>

Inputs: mechanisms, functions, targeted manufacturing cost

Outputs: mechanisms targeted for cost reduction

Background of the chart

When you think about it, this chart is where the design process used to start. What was the product to do and what mechanisms would perform that function? The chart is enhanced by carrying through the weighting numbers from the customer demands and using them to help determine the importance of each mechanism.

Its role in product design

This chart is a key chart in checking to see that the mechanisms are in place to support the functions that will be performed. It also provides the relative value of each mechanism.

First Level of Detail

Mechanisms

Chart C-2 Pencil example	Function weight	Writing mechanism	Erasing mechanism	Lead holding mechanism	Chewing mechanism	
write	54%	◎ 486	Δ 54	◎ 486	○ 162	
erase	34%	○ 102	◎ 306	Δ 34	Δ 34	
chewing	3%		Δ 3	○ 9	◎ 27	
pointing	9%		Δ 9	◎ 81		
mechanism raw weight		588	372	610	223	1793
mechanism %		33%	21%	34%	12%	
mechanism value		4¢	2.5¢	4¢	1.5¢	12¢
mechanism actual cost		4¢	4¢	3¢	2¢	13¢

(left side label: **Functions**)

Figure 13.1 Pencil example Chart C-2

Comments

1. The key mechanism is the lead-holding mechanism.

2. The number 2 mechanism is the writing mechanism (lead).

3. The erasing mechanism is a target for cost reduction: 4¢ vs. 2.5¢.

Instructions for filling out Chart C-2

1. List the mechanisms from Chart C-1.

2. List the functions from Chart A-2.

3. List the function weights from Chart B-1.

4. Use a double circle, or 9, to indicate the strong correlations between mechanisms and functions. Also multiply that value times the function weight and place in the box.

5. Add the mechanism weights in each column.

6 Convert mechanism weights to a percentage by adding the row and dividing the total into each number.

7. Multiply the mechanism weight percentage times the targeted cost from 8. List mechanism value.

  Compare the actual costs with the targeted cost and use value engineering on those mechanisms that are higher than targeted.

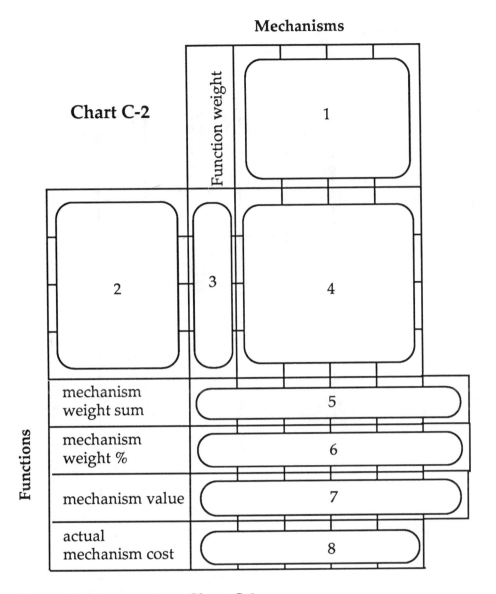

Figure 13.2 Instructions Chart C-2

Mechanisms

Chart C-2

	Function weight				
mechanism weight sum					
mechanism weight %					
mechanism value					
actual mechanism cost					

Functions (label on left side)

Figure 13.3 Practice Chart C-2

Suggestions

Use this chart to consider whether there are other alternatives for mechanisms.

Chapter 14

Chart C-3   Mechanisms/ Quality Characteristics

Chart C-3 shows how the mechanisms relate to the quality characteristics and determines the relative cost value of each quality characteristic.

Description of the chart

Chart C-3 is a matrix. On the top are the mechanisms which were first listed in Chart C-1. On the left are the quality characteristics which were highlighted in Chart B-3. The strong correlations are identified with a double circle, or a 9. The cases of some correlation are indicated with a circle, or a 3. The instances of possible correlation are indicated with a triangle, or 1. The right column of the chart indicates the expected value of each quality characteristic.

Purpose of the chart

The purpose of the chart is to identify which mechanisms most relate to the quality characteristics which were highlighted for breakthrough.

Summary

Inputs: mechanisms, key quality characteristics

Outputs: mechanisms to focus on in achieving breakthroughs

Background of the chart

This chart grew out of the need to quickly find areas where it might be possible to get the breakthroughs sought by the QFD study.

Its role in product design

This chart is the key to find which mechanisms to look to in terms of breakthroughs.

Sample of Chart C-3

First level of detail

	wt.	**Chart C-3** Pencil Example	writing mechanism	erasing mechanism	lead holding mechanism	chewing mechanism	quality char. value
key quality characteristics							
	41%	time between sharpening	◎		◎		5 ¢
	30%	lead dust generated	◎		Δ		3.6¢
						Total	12¢

Figure 14.1 Pencil example Chart C-3

Instructions for filling out Chart C-3

1. List the mechanisms from Chart C-1.

2. List the Quality Characteristics from Chart B-3.

3. Use a double circle, or 9, to indicate the strong correlations between mechanisms and quality characteristics. Use a circle, or 3, to indicate some correlation. Use a triangle, or 1, to indicate possible correlation.

4. Multiply the quality characteristic weights from Chart A-1 times the target cost and put the answer in this column

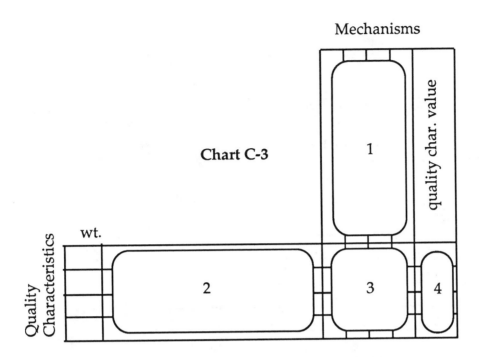

Figure 14.2 Instructions Chart C-3

Practice Chart C-3

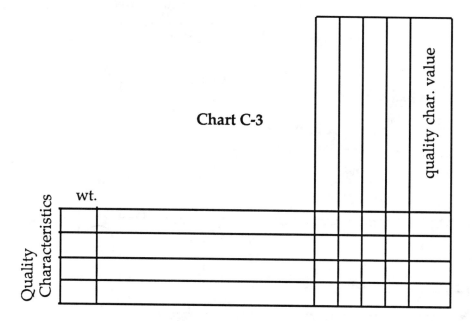

Figure 14.3 Practice Chart C-3

Chapter 15

Chart C-4   Mechanisms vs. Parts

Chart C-4 shows how mechanisms relate to parts.

Description of the chart

Chart C-4 is a matrix. On the top are the mechanisms which were first listed in Chart C-1. On the left is the full list of parts from Chart A-4. The strong correlations are identified with a double circle, or 9. The cases of some correlation are indicated with a circle, or 3. The instances of possible correlation are indicated with a triangle, or 1. The right column of the chart indicates the targeted value of each part.

Purpose of the chart

The purpose of the chart is to establish the value of each part.

Summary

Inputs: mechanisms, parts

Outputs: focus on cost reduction of parts

Background of the chart

This chart grew out of the need to better identify the value of the parts--a 1980's chart.

Its role in product design

This chart prioritizes part cost reduction.

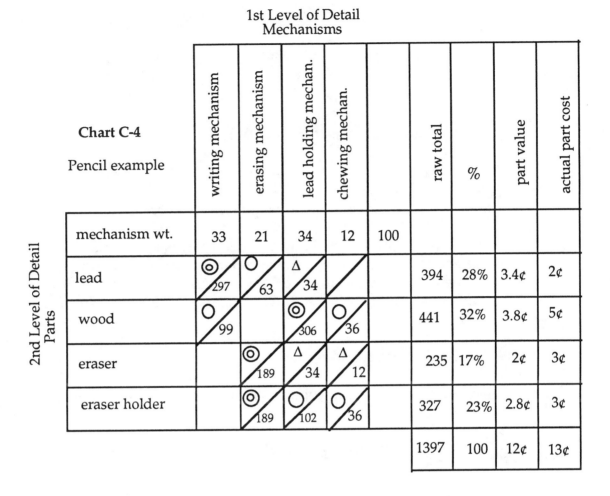

Figure 15.1 Pencil example Chart C-4

<u>Comments</u>

1. The wood is a target for cost control because it costs 1.2¢ more than it should (5¢ - 3.8¢).

2. The eraser is a target for cost control because it costs 50% more than it should (3¢ vs. 2¢).

<u>Instructions for filling out Chart C-4</u>

1. List the mechanisms from Chart C-1.

2. List the parts from Chart A-4.

3. Bring down mechanism weights from Chart C-2.

4. Record correlations between mechanisms and parts: double circle, or 9, for strong correlation; circle, or 3, for some correlation; triangle, or 1, for possible correlation. Multiply each item times the mechanism weight (%) from Chart C-2.

5. Total weights, adding across.

6. Add weights (sum column 4) and divide into each part weight.

7. Multiply parts weight (%) times target cost from Chart B-2. Compare with actual.

8. Record actual parts weight. Do value engineering on parts whose actual part cost is higher than part value.

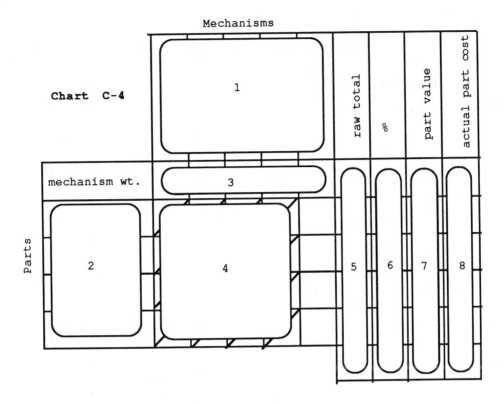

Figure 15.2 Instructions Chart C-4

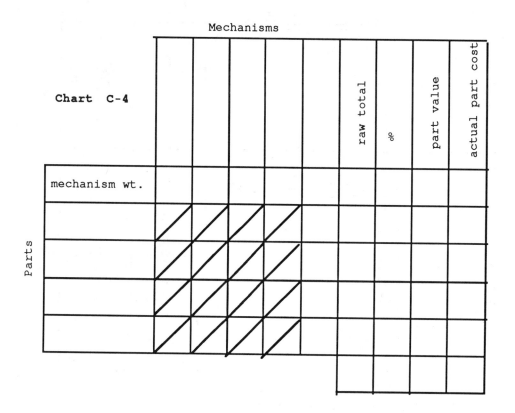

Figure 15.3 Practice Chart C-4

Comments

     This chart provides a good opportunity to check the connections between mechanisms and parts. They should flow, with parts being one level of detail greater than mechanisms.

Chapter 16

Chart D-1   Product Failure Modes
vs.
Customer   Demands

Description of the chart

Chart D-1 is a matrix. On the top are product failure modes which were generated by a Fault Tree Analysis. On the left are the customer demands from Chart A-1. The strong correlations are identified with a double circle, or 9. The cases of some correlation are indicated with a circle, or 3. The instances of possible correlation are indicated with a triangle, or 1. The bottom row equals the priority of product failure modes based on customer demands.

Purpose of the chart

The purpose of the chart is to prioritize product failure modes for reliability engineering.

Summary

Inputs: product failure modes, customer demands

Outputs: priority of failure modes

Background of the chart

The chart was developed in the early 1980's to tie reliability engineering to QFD. This chart was also added because the prioritization of items in Chart A-1 led to the dropping of items. This chart picks those up.

Its role in product design

Prioritizing reliability engineering is important so that the work of reliability engineers is focused.

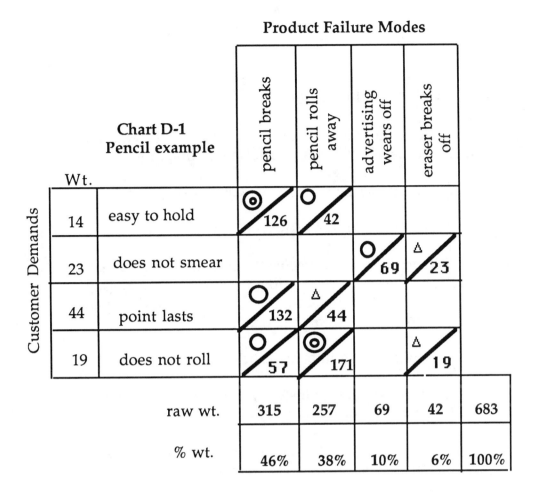

Figure 16.1 Pencil example Chart D-1

<u>Comments</u>

1. The pencil breaking is the most important product failure mode to work on (46%) from the view of customer demands.

2. The pencil rolling away is the second most important product failure mode to work on (38%) from the view of customer demands.

Instructions for filling out Chart D-1

1. Brainstorm failure modes. Do a Fault Tree Analysis.[1]
List three levels in the format of a tree diagram.

2. List customer demands from Chart A-1.

3. Transfer demanded weight from Chart A-1.

4. Do correlations: double circle, or 9, is strong correlation;
circle, or 3, is some correlation; triangle, or 1, is possible
correlation. Multiply each item by the demanded quality
weight from column 3.

5. Add weighted numbers vertically.

6. Convert weighted sums (row 4) to percentages by
adding across and dividing total into each item.

   The highest percentages represent the failure
modes prioritized by customer demands.

---

[1] See Chapter 24

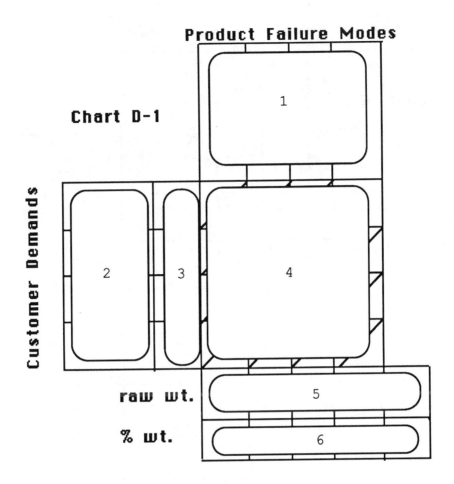

Figure 16.2 Instructions Chart D-1

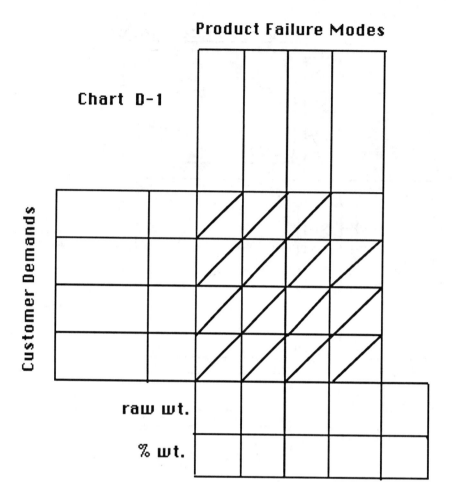

Figure 16.3 Practice Chart D-1

Suggestions

1. On the FTA (Fault Tree Analysis) it is good to go 4 or 5 levels, but just take the first three levels for Chart D-1. This helps get an even level of detail on failure modes.

2. It is very easy to confuse product failure modes with parts failure modes. Parts failure modes are in Chart D-4.

Chapter 17

Chart D-2   Product Failure Modes vs. Functions

Chart D-2 shows how product failure modes relate to product functions.

Description of the chart

Chart D-2 is a matrix. On the top are product failure modes from Chart D-1. On the left side are functions from Chart A-2. The strong correlations are identified with a double circle, or 9. The cases of some correlations are identified with a single circle, or 3. The instances of possible correlations are indicated with a triangle, or 1. The bottom row equals the priority of product failure modes based on product functions.

Purpose of the chart

The purpose of the chart is to prioritize product failure modes for reliability engineering.

Summary

Inputs: product failure modes, product functions

Outputs: priority of failure modes

Background of the chart

The chart was added in the 1980's to tie QFD into reliability engineering and to assure that some items were not lost by prioritizing customer demands.

Its role in product design

Products need to be reliable. Engineers need to focus on key issues.

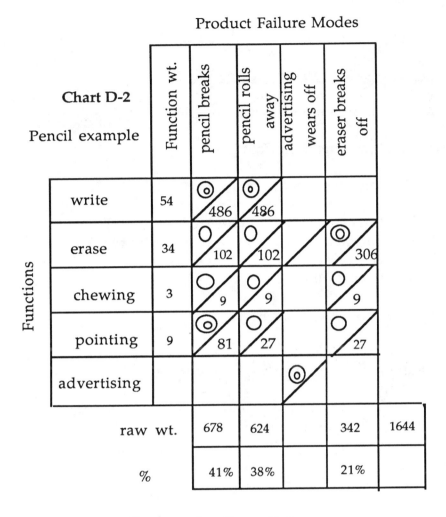

Figure 17.1   Pencil example Chart D-2

<u>Comments</u>

1. The first priority for product reliability study is "pencil breaks" (41%) as it relates to product function.

2. The second priority for product reliability study is "pencil rolls away" (38%) as it relates to product function.

Note: The product failure mode of "advertising wears off" suggests that the function of advertising should be added to the list.

Instructions for filling out Chart D-2

1. List failure modes from Chart D-1.

2. List functions from Chart A-2.

3. List function weights from Chart B-1.

4. Do correlations: double circle, or 9, is strong correlation; circle, or 3, is some correlation; triangle, or 1, is possible correlation. Multiply each item by the function weight from column 2.

5. Add weighted numbers vertically.

6. Convert weighted sums (row 5) to percentages by adding across and dividing total into each item.

   The highest percentages represent the failure modes prioritized by functions.

Product Failure Modes

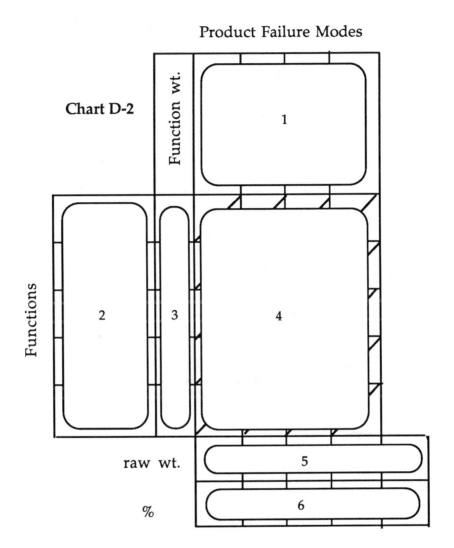

Figure 17.2 Instructions Chart D-2

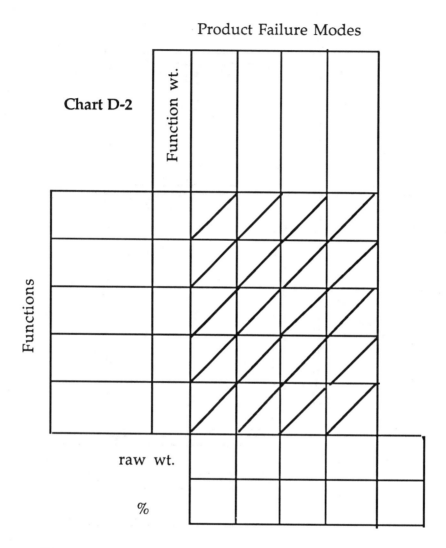

Figure 17.3 Practice Chart D-2

Suggestions

Because of its focus on function, this chart also has some interesting correlations with value analysis.

Chapter   18

Chart D-3   Product   Failure   Modes
vs.
Quality   Characteristics

Chart D-3 shows how product failure modes relate to quality characteristics.

<u>Description of the chart</u>

Chart D-3 is a matrix. On the top are product failure modes from Chart D-1. On the left side are quality characteristics from Chart A-1. The strong correlations are identified with a double circle, or 9. The cases of some correlation are identified with single circle, or 3. The instances of possible correlation are indicated with a triangle, or 1. The total on the bottom row represents the priority of product failure modes based on quality characteristics.

<u>Purpose of the chart</u>

The purpose of the chart is to prioritize product failure modes for reliability engineering.

<u>Summary</u>

Inputs: product failure modes, quality characteristics

Outputs: priority of failure modes

Background of the chart

The chart was added in the 1980's to tie reliability engineering and QFD together, and to assure that some items were not lost by prioritizing quality characteristics.

Its role in product design

Products need to be reliable. Engineers need to focus on key issues.

Example Chart D-3

Product Failure Modes

Chart D-3 Pencil example	Function wt.	pencil breaks	pencil rolls away	advertising wears off	eraser breaks off
length	9		Δ / 9		
time between sharpening	41	◎ / 369			
lead dust generated	30				
hexagonality	19	Δ / 19	◎ / 171		

Quality Characteristics

raw wt.		388	180		568
%		68	32		

Figure 18.1 Pencil example Chart D-3

Comments

1. Pencil breaks is a major problem (69%).

2. Pencil rolls away is an important item (31%).

3. The blanks in column "advertising wears off" and "eraser breaks off" suggest there may be some missing quality characteristics, such as durability of advertising and torque strength of eraser. This shows the self-correcting nature of charts where one raises questions about another.

Instructions for filling out Chart D-3

1. List failure modes from Chart D-1.

2. List quality characteristics from Chart A-3.

3. List quality characteristics weights from Chart A-1.

4. Do correlations: double circle, or 9, is strong correlation; circle, or 3, is some correlation; triangle, or 1, is possible correlation. Multiply each item by the quality characteristic weight in column 3.

5. Add weighted numbers vertically.

6. Convert weighted sums (row 4) to percentages by adding across and dividing total into each item.

    The highest percentages represent the failure modes prioritized by quality characteristics.

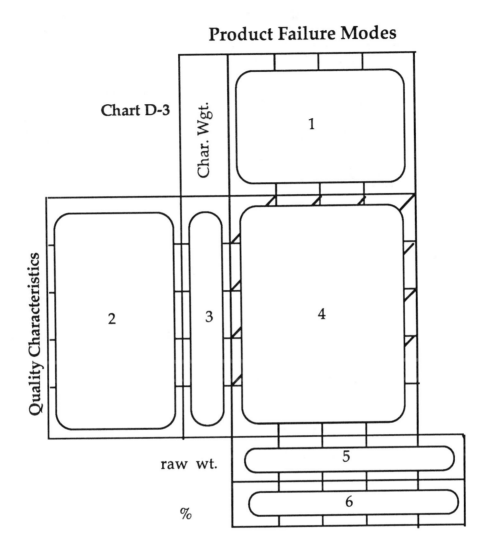

Figure 18.2 Instructions Chart D-3

Product Failure Modes

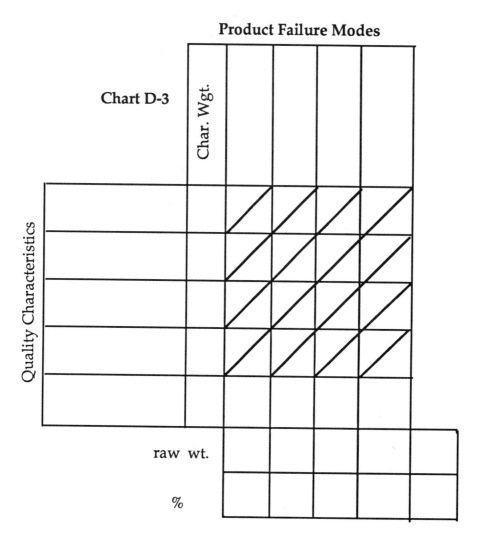

Figure 18.3 Practice Chart D-3

Comments

Review any failure modes where there are no quality characteristics to see if there are missing quality characteristics.

Chapter 19

Chart D-4   Parts Failure Modes and Parts

Chart D-4 shows how parts failure modes relate to parts.

<u>Description of the chart</u>

Chart D-4 is a matrix. On the top are parts failure modes. On the left are parts from Chart A-4. Use a double circle, or 9, for strong correlation; a single circle, or 3, for some correlation; and a triangle, or 1, for possible correlation. On the right column are project numbers referring to FMEA project numbers.

<u>Purpose of the chart</u>

The purpose of the chart is to prioritize FMEA studies by identifying the correlation between parts failure modes and parts.

<u>Summary</u>

Inputs: parts failure modes, parts

Outputs: priority of FMEA projects to do on parts

Background of the chart

The chart was added in the 1980's to tie reliability engineering to QFD. This chart made it possible to prioritize FMEA parts projects.[1]

Its role in product design

Parts need to be reliable. Engineers need to focus on critical parts.

---

[1] Yoji Akao, Norio Komizawa (1976): "Quality Function Deployment and FMEA Quality Control, Vol. 30, No. 8, pp. 12-18.

Example

Parts Failure Modes

Chart D-4 Pencil example	parts wt.	breaks	falls apart	smudges	wears out	gross wt.	%	FMEA project #
lead	28	⊚ / 252		◯ / 84	⊙ / 252	588	31%	401
wood	32	⊙ / 288	⊙ / 288			576	31%	402
eraser	17	◯ / 153	◯ / 51	⊙ / 153	⊙ / 153	510	27%	403
eraser holder	23		⊚ / 207			207	11%	404
						1881	100%	

Parts

Figure 19.1 Pencil example Chart D-4

Comments

1. The top priority FMEA project is #401 lead (with a gross weight of 588 or 31%).

2. The next priority FMEA project is #402 (with a gross weight of 576 or 31%). Notice that the eraser, although it has more correlations, comes in third as a result of its lower weighting.

Instructions for filling out Chart D-4

1. Brainstorm parts failure modes. Construct affinity and tree diagram and record to the third level of detail.

2. List parts from Chart A-4.

3. List parts weight from Chart C-4.

4. Do correlations: double circle, or 9, is strong correlation; circle, or 3, is some correlation; triangle, or 1, is possible correlation. Multiply each item by the parts weight from Column 3.

5. Add weighted numbers horizontally.

6. Convert weighted sums (column 4) to percentages by adding down and dividing total into each item.

   The highest percentages represent the failure modes by parts.

7. List the reference numbers of the FMEA chart[2] that investigate and record action taken on each of the most critical failure modes.

---

[2]   See Chapter 32 for explanations and examples of Process FMEA charts.

Parts Failure Modes

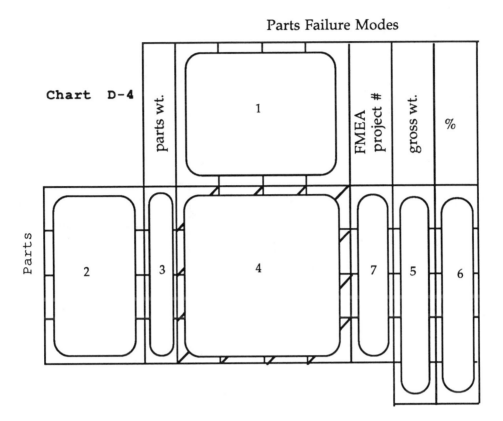

Figure 19.2 Instructions Chart D-4

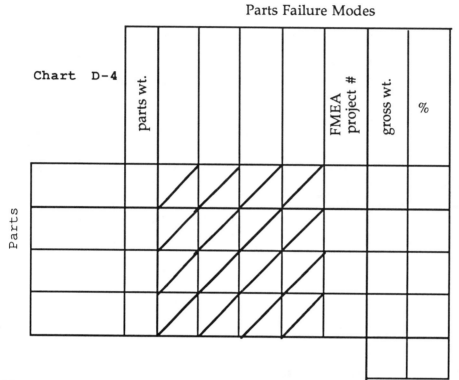

Figure 19.3 Practice Chart D-4

Comments

Note that the use of weighted numbers does have an effect on the analysis in the example on page 19-3. Without the weights, eraser would have come out higher than lead and wood.

Chapter 20

Chart E-1 New Concept Selection and Customer Demands

Chart E-1 shows how new concepts relate to customer demands.

Description of the chart

Chart E-1 is a matrix. On the top are new concepts. On the left side are customer demands. In the middle column is the standard for each customer demand. The pluses (+) and minuses (-) indicate whether the new concept is better or worse than the standard. The totals at the bottom of the page make it possible to evaluate the relative strengths and weaknesses of each new concept.

Purpose of the chart

The purpose of the chart is to identify new concepts that will positively relate to customer demands without causing other problems.

Summary

Inputs: new concepts, customer demands

Outputs: value of new concepts

Background of the chart

A system of new concept selection was made popular by Stuart Pugh of Scotland. He observed that engineers sometimes hold on tenaciously to their favorite engineering solutions. He developed this new concept matrix to assist teams of engineers to review new concepts more objectively.

Its role in product design

New concepts are most important for design. Stuart Pugh[1] suggests that in brand new products the new concept development should be done before Chart A-1. This avoids the danger of being limited in thinking by present technology or products. In the case of product upgrade it is the author's opinion that it be used after the preliminary product definition. Hence its position in column E.

---

[1] Stuart Pugh has contributed significant ideas in new concept selection. The reader is referred to the following paper: Stuart Pugh, Concept Selection - A Method That Works, (Rome, Italy: International Conference on Engineering Design ICED 81), 1981.
    The application of new concept selection to QFD shows promise to both Mr. Pugh and the author. How the two can best be integrated is not yet fully clear. References to Mr. Pugh's ideas does not infer his agreement with the approach currently used in this book. Later editions of this book or a separate book by Mr. Pugh may help. In the interim these preliminary attempts have proved of benefit in QFD and are therefore included.

New Concepts

Chart E-1 Pencil example (Customer Demands)	spring loaded lead	retractable lead	Datum best in class	friction fit eraser	pocket clip	china pencil
easy to hold			Quill		–	
does not smear		+	E. F.			–
point lasts	+	+				–
does not roll					+	–
Cost	-	-		+	-	+
+'s	1+	2+		1+	1+	1+
– 's	1-	1-			2-	3–

Figure 20.1 Pencil example Chart E-1

Comments

1. Retractable lead looks promising (2 pluses).

2. China pencil (thick lead exposed by peeling outside) does not look good (3 minuses).

3. Datum may be best own product, best competitor product or best in class product for each criterion.

Instructions for filling out Chart E-1

1. Brainstorm new concepts. Do affinity and tree diagram.
List first three levels.

2. List customer demands from Chart A-1.

3. List any data on best in class.

4. Use a "plus" (+) if the new concept would better meet a
customer demand than the current product or service.
Use an "S" if it would meet a customer demand in a
similar way. Use a minus (-) if the new concept would
meet a customer demand less than an existing
product.

5. Add the pluses (+) in the column and enter total.

6. Add the minuses (-) in the column and enter the total.
If the concept is selected refer the minuses (-) to column F
for optimization.

Note: Do not combine pluses (+) and minuses (-) to give a
net gain or loss. It is important to see the total number of
pluses (+) and minuses (-).

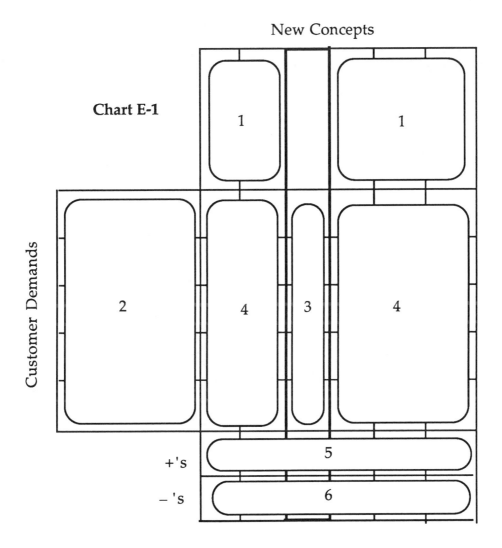

Figure 20.2 Instructions Chart E-1

New Concepts

Chart E-1

Customer Demands

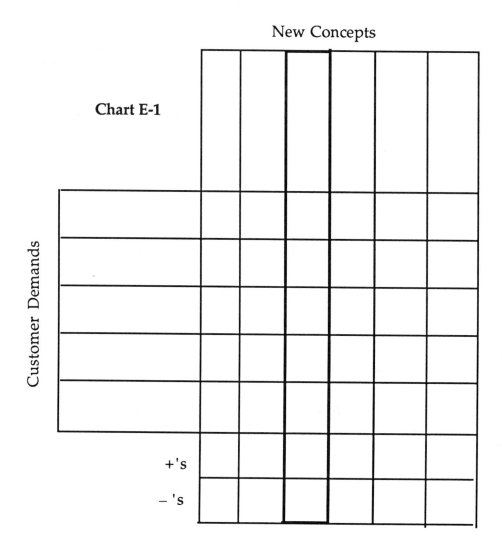

+'s

− 's

Figure 20.3 Practice Chart C-1

<u>Comments</u>

1. The best in class can be selected by identifying one product with which you are competing. Alternately you may pick the competition who is best in class for each item.

2. If there are no new concepts which relate to a criterion, then perhaps more work needs to be done in identifying new concepts that relate to that criterion. In the example there are no new concepts for "easy to hold".

Chapter 21

Chart E-2   New Concept Selection and Functions

Chart E-2 shows how new concepts relate to product functions.

Description of the chart

Chart E-2 is a matrix. On the top are new concepts. On the left side are product functions. In the middle column is the standard for each function. The pluses (+) and minuses (-) indicate whether the new concept is better or worse than the standard. The totals at the bottom of the page make it possible to evaluate the relative strengths and weaknesses of each new concept.

Purpose of the chart

The purpose of the chart is to identify new concepts that will positively relate to product function without causing other problems.

Summary

Inputs: new concepts, functions

Outputs: value of new concepts

<u>Background of the chart</u>

The system of new concept selection was made popular by Stuart Pugh of Scotland. He observed that engineers sometimes hold on tenaciously to their favorite engineering solutions. He developed this new concept matrix to assist teams of engineers to review new concepts more objectively.

<u>Its role in product design</u>

New concepts are most important for design. Stuart Pugh suggests that in brand new products the new concept development should be done before Chart A-1. This avoids the danger of being limited in thinking by present technology or products. In the case of product upgrade it is the author's opinion that it be used after the preliminary product definition. Hence its position in column E.

Example E-2

New Concepts

Chart E-2 Pencil example	spring loaded lead	retractable lead	best in class	friction fit eraser	pocket clip	china pencil
write	+	+				
erase				+		−
chewing					+	−
pointing						
+'s	1+	1+		1+	1+	
−'s						2−

Functions

Figure 21.1 Pencil example Chart E-2

Instructions for filling out Chart E-2

1. List new concepts from Chart E-1.

2. List functions from Chart A-2.

3. List best in class.

4. Use a plus (+) if the new concept would better meet functions less effectively than an existing product. Use an "S" or leave blank if the new concept meets functions in a similar way to existing products. Use a minus (-) if it is worse than existing product as regards function.

5. Add the pluses (+) in the column and enter the total. If the concept is selected refer the minuses (-) to column F for optimization.

6. Add the minuses (-) in the column and enter the total. If the concept is selected refer the minuses (-) to column F for optimization.

Note: Do not combine pluses (+) and minuses (-). Each of the minuses (-) needs to be investigated to see if it can be eliminated. The goal is to make improvements without creating other problems.

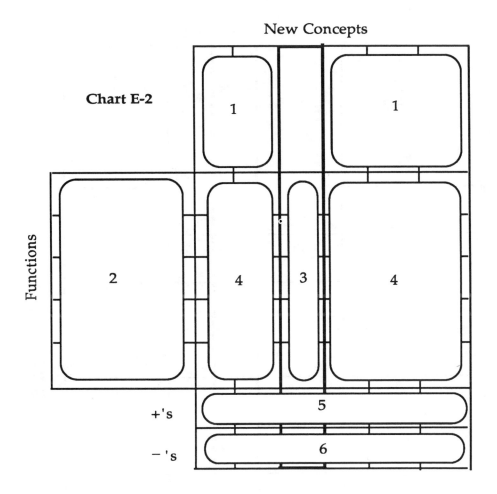

Figure 21.2 Instructions Chart E-2

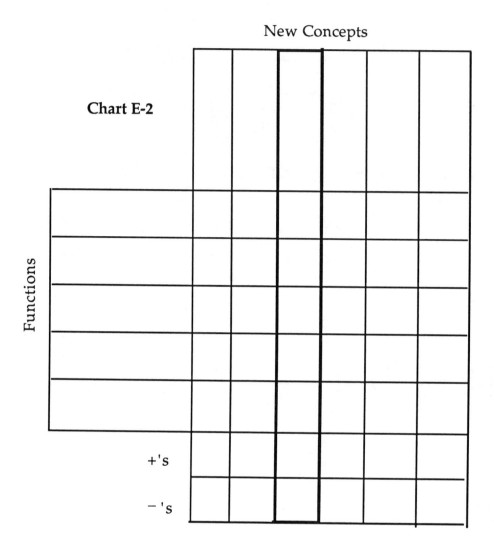

Figure 21.3 Practice Chart E-2

Comments

This idea can be tied to value analysis because of the focus on function.

Chapter 22

Chart E-3   New Concept Selection and Quality Characteristics

Chart E-3 shows how new concepts relate to quality characteristics.

Description of the chart

Chart E-3 is a matrix. On the top are new concepts. On the left side are quality characteristics. In the middle is the standard for each quality characteristic. The pluses (+) and minuses (-) indicate whether the new concept is better or worse than the standard. The totals at the bottom of the page make it possible to evaluate the relative strengths and weaknesses of each new concept.

Purpose of the chart

The purpose of the chart is to identify new concepts that help meet quality characteristics and to identify voids where new concepts need to be developed.

Summary

Inputs: new concepts and quality characteristics

Outputs: new concepts that show promise; also negative aspects of new concepts that need to be minimized

Background of the chart

The system of new concept selection was made popular by Stuart Pugh of Scotland. He observed that engineers sometimes hold on tenaciously to their favorite engineering solutions. He developed this new concept matrix to assist teams of engineers to review new concepts more objectively.

Its role in product design

New concepts are most important for design. Stuart Pugh suggests that in brand new products the new concept development should be done before Chart A-1. This avoids the danger of being limited in thinking by present technology or products. In the case of product upgrade it is the author's opinion that it be used after the preliminary product definition. Hence its position in column E.

Example E-3

New Concepts

Chart 3

Pencil example

Quality Characteristics	spring loaded lead	retractable lead	best in class	friction fit eraser	pocket clip	china pencil
length		+				
time between sharpening	+	+				–
lead dust generated	+	+				–
hexagonality	–					–
+'s	2+	3+		1+	1+	
– 's	1–					3–

Figure 22.1 Pencil example Chart E-3

<u>Comments</u>

1. Retractable lead (3 +'s) looks good as does spring loaded lead (2 +'s).

2. China pencil does not look good.

3. Pocket clip and friction fit eraser do not have any correlations. Consider possibility that quality characteristics should be added.

Instructions for filling out Chart E-3

1. List new concepts from Chart E-1.

2. List quality characteristics from Chart A-3.

3. Fill in "best in class".

4. Use a plus (+) if the new concept would better meet a quality characteristic than the current product or service. Use a minus (-) if the new concept would meet a quality characteristic less effectively than an existing product. Use an "S" or leave blank if the new concept meets quality characteristics in a similar way to existing product.

5. Add the pluses (+) in the column and enter the total.

6. Add the minuses (-) in the column and enter the total. If the concept is selected refer the minuses (-) to column F for optimization.

Note: Do not combine pluses (+) and minuses (-). It is important to see these totals separately to evaluate them.

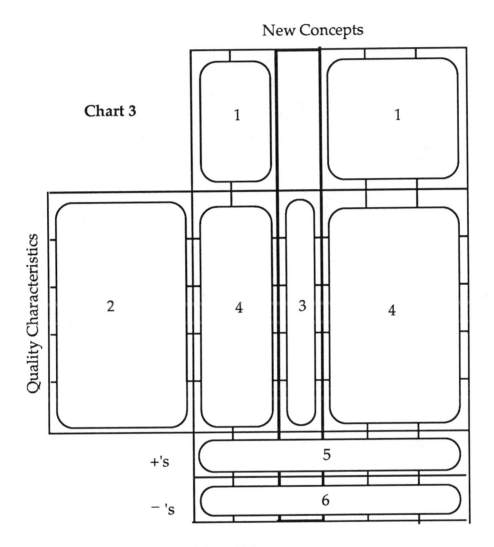

Figure 22.2 Instructions Chart E-3

Practice chart

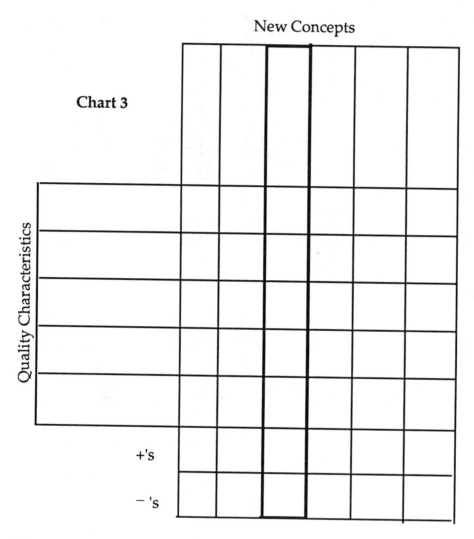

Figure 22.3 Practice Chart E-3

Comments

Cost can also be added as a helpful and important criterion.

Chapter 23

Chart E-4   New Concept Selection Totals

Chart E-4 shows the totals of each of the charts on "new concept selection" in column E.

Description of chart

Chart E-4 is a matrix. On the top are new concepts. On the left are the various sets of criteria from column E. The pluses (+) and minuses (-) indicate whether the new concept is better or worse than the standard. The totals at the bottom of the page make it possible to evaluate the relative strengths and weaknesses of each new concept.

Purpose of the chart

The purpose of the chart is to identify new concepts that will positively relate to all the criteria in column E without causing other problems.

Summary

Inputs: totals from column E

Outputs: grand total for new concept selection

Background of the chart

The system of new concept selection was made popular by Stuart Pugh of Scotland. He observed that engineers sometimes hold on tenaciously to their favorite engineering solutions. He developed this new concept matrix to assist teams of engineers to review new concepts more objectively.

Its role in product design

New concepts are most important for design. Stuart Pugh suggests that in brand new products the new concept development should be done before Chart A-1. This avoids the danger of being limited in thinking by present technology or products. In the case of product upgrade it is the author's opinion that it be used after the preliminary product definition. Hence its position in column E.

Example E-4

New Concepts

Chart 4 Pencil example	spring loaded lead	retractable lead	(Datum) best in class	friction fit eraser	pocket clip	china pencil
customer demands	1+	2+			1+	3 –
functions	1+	1+		1+	1+	2–
quality characteristics	2+	3+				3–
Total +'s –'s	4+	6+		1+	2+	8 –

Summary

Figure 23.1 Pencil example Chart C-4

<u>Comments:</u>

1. The retractable lead (6+, 0-) and the spring loaded lead (4+, 0-) both look very promising.

2. The china pencil does not look like a viable replacement concept (8-).

Instructions for filling out Chart E-4

1. List new concepts from Chart E-1.

2. List the "best in class".

3. List total pluses (+) and minuses (-) from Charts E-1, E-2, E-3.

4. Total the columns of pluses (+).

5. Total the columns of minuses (-).

   Select new concepts with large numbers of pluses (+). Refer minuses (-) in selected concepts to following charts in column F for optimization.

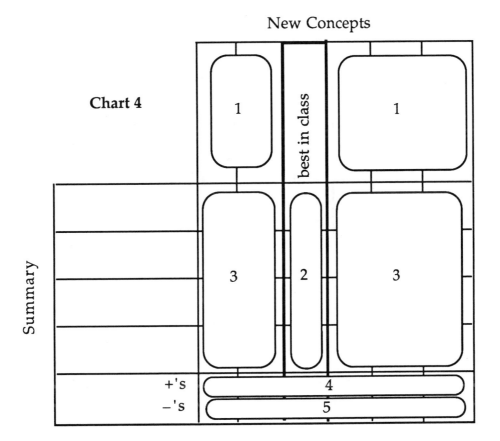

Figure 23.2 Instructions Chart E-4

New Concepts

Chart 4

best in class

Summary

+'s
−'s

Figure 23.3 Practice Chart E-4

Chapter 24

Cost Breakthroughs/Value Engineering

Introduction

Value engineering is a recommended system of cost reduction associated with Quality Function Deployment. The weighting system developed by Yoji Akao and the author provides a format for determining the value of functions, quality characteristics, mechanisms and parts. These can be identified in the following charts:

B-1: the value of the function
C-2: the value of the mechanism
C-3: the value of quality characteristic
C-4: the value of parts

The weighting system used in these charts takes into account customer demands, areas where the company needs to improve vs. the competition, and the major and minor sales points that the company has selected for the product.

There are several phases in value analysis:

1. Organization Phase
2. Information Phase
3. Innovation Phase
4. Evaluation Phase
5. Implementation Phase[1]

---

[1] This outline is based on ideas shared with the author by M. Larry Shillito of Eastman Kodak Company at the August 1987 GOAL/QPC QFD course.

Value engineering may be defined as "an organized effort directed at analyzing the function of systems, equipment, and supplies to achieve the required function at the lowest overall cost consistent with requirements for performance, reliability and maintainability."

Organization Phase

The organization phase suggests that the Value Analysis project should be set up with the right people doing the right things in the right way. This may be common sense but common sense is not always common.

1. Project definition: The project should be defined as clearly as possible. What is the problem being solved? What are its objectives and how will they be addressed?

2. Who will do the project? The team should consist of three to seven members and be interdisciplinary. It should involve the people knowledgeable about the product or service regardless of place in the organization. It should involve someone who can make decisions and someone who can facilitate the process.

3. Focusing on the right issues: List the main components and their functions. Refer to QFD Chart B-4.

Information phase

The information phase of value analysis determines the value of each function in a tree type diagram called the FAST system. As was indicated above, QFD contains these values identified in Charts B-1, C-2, C-3 and C-4.

The value engineering system uses the FAST system--short for Functional Analysis Systems Technique. This system is a tree type structure which breaks down the values of each function. It would only be used in QFD as a cross check of the values in Chart B-1.

Once these numbers are established they are put on the Value Graph.

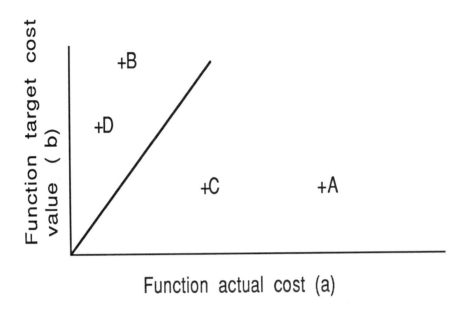

Figure 24.1 Value Analysis Chart

The priority area A contains the items that have relatively low importance and relatively high cost.

Another system for finding the function weight is to look at each two functions side by side and decide which one is more important. Putting this information together establishes the relative importance of each function.

Innovation phase

Once the targets for reduction have been established, the next phase is to get breakthroughs. This is the creative part and a valuable part of the redesign process.

Some of the traditional methods include:

a. <u>Brainstorming</u>: In brainstorming the group lists ideas for reducing the cost without discussing or critiquing them. All the generation of ideas may be expanded by systematically going around the room giving participants the opportunity to suggest an idea or pass on to the next person.

b. <u>Nominal Group Technique:</u> This is a way of prioritizing ideas. First ideas are brainstormed as above. Then similar ideas are grouped together. The number of items to be ranked is selected using the formula of 1/2 + 1. That means that if there are, for example, 15 items left after the combining, then 8 items are ranked. Each person then votes for their preference of items. (In the example above each person gives 8 points to their top priority idea, 7 points to their second priority item and so on.) Items are totalled and plotted in a pareto chart (i.e., a bar chart is created listing the totals for each item in descending order.) The number of people voting for each item can also be indicated.

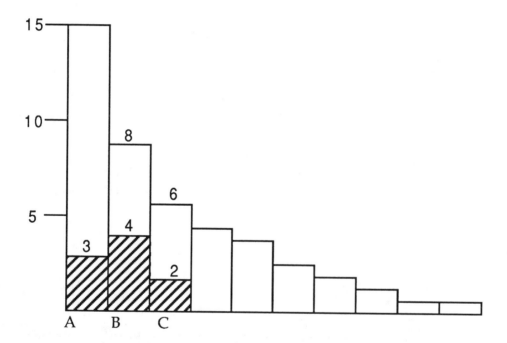

Figure 24.2 Example of Nominal Group Technique Report

In the example, Item A got 15 points and 3 participants voted for it; Item B received 8 points and 4 voted for it; Item C received 6 points and 2 voted for it.

c. <u>Test for value</u>: Every material, every part, every operation must pass these tests:

1) Can we do without it?
2) Does it do more than is required?
3) Does it cost more than it is worth?
4) Is there something better to do the job?
5) Can it be made by a less costly method?
6) Can a standard item be used?
7) Considering the quantities used, could a less costly tooling method be used?
8) Does it cost more than the total of reasonable labor, overhead material and profit?
9) Can someone else provide it at lower cost without affecting dependability?
10) If it were your money, would you refuse to buy the item because it cost too much?

d. <u>Ten Commandments of possibility thinking</u>:

1) Never reject a possibility because you see something wrong with it.

2) Never reject a possibility because you won't get credit.

3) Never reject a possibility because it is impossible.

4) Never reject a possibility because your mind is already made up.

5) Never reject an idea because it is illegal--change the law!

6) Never reject an idea because you don't have the money, manpower, muscle or months to achieve it.

7) Never reject an idea because it will cause conflict.

8) Never reject an idea because it's not your way of doing things.

9) Never reject an idea because it might fail.

10) Never reject an idea because it is sure to succeed.

Evaluation phase

This is an important phase because if you hedge on value to reduce cost, the whole system will suffer and it will take a long time to get back quality reputation.

Step 1: Prescreening. Focus on the best suggestions by voting. Each person would normally select 20%. Another option is to put each item on a separate card and sort the cards by value.

Step 2: Criterion Analysis: In this stage ideas are evaluated by a criterion such as ease of use, ease of manufacture, safety, quality, attractiveness, government regulations, or ecological considerations.

Similar tools include decision trees, delphi, etc.

Implementation phase

The implementation phase involves selling the idea, making the change and making sure that the improvement is long lasting.

The implementation can be facilitated by a well documented report. Having the key decision maker as part of the team is also a big plus.

The implementation effectiveness can also be improved by using an arrow diagram or a PDPC.

Chapter 25

Chart F-2 Fault Tree Analysis and Reliability Breakthroughs

The FTA (Fault Tree Analysis) lists the potential failures and subfailures in a logical way.

Description

The Fault Tree Analysis is an upside down tree-type figure with failure modes broken down into increasing levels of detail. Two hat-like symbols are used. The one with the line straight across the bottom indicates "and" (⌂). The one with the curved line on the bottom represents "or" (⌒)

Purpose

The purpose of the chart is to systematically identify and portray relationships between failure modes so that failure modes are not missed, and so that there can be focus on root causes rather than symptoms.

Summary

Inputs: broad failure modes

Outputs: detailed causes of product failure

Background of the chart

The chart originally was strongly used in the safety field and has a long history in reliability engineering. It was combined with Q.F.D. in the mid 1980's as a result of the work of Macabe and Akao.

Role in design engineering

A high level of reliability is important in design and that needs to be addressed in a systematic way. The more popular FMEA Failure Mode and Effect Analysis indicates the priority of failures to work on in terms of severity, frequency and detectability. The FTA Fault Tree Analysis gives a picture of the interrelationship between failures. This helps make sure that potential failures are not missed and shows the interrelationship between major and minor causes of failures.

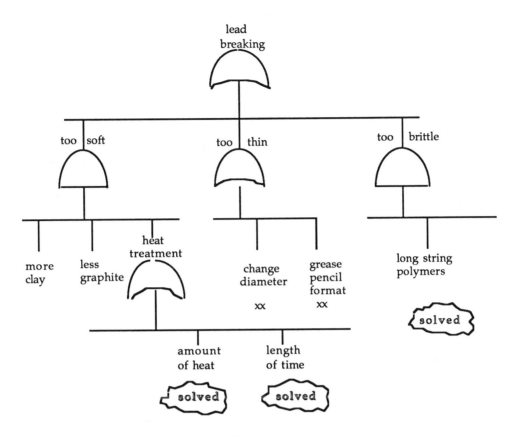

Figure 25.1 Pencil example Chart F-2

Instructions for Chart F-2

1. List product failure modes and arrange in a tree type chart with a straight bottom hat symbol representing "and" and a curved bottom hat symbol representing "or".

2. List causes of problems and arrange in a tree type chart using the same symbols as instruction #1 above.

3. Indicate dead ends to solutions with an "x" and solutions with the word "solution" surrounded by a rough circle.[1]

---

[1] This use of the Fault Tree Analysis to indicate solutions and dead ends is referred to as the PDPC (Process Decision Program Chart) See Appendix, page A-61.

Fault Tree Analysis

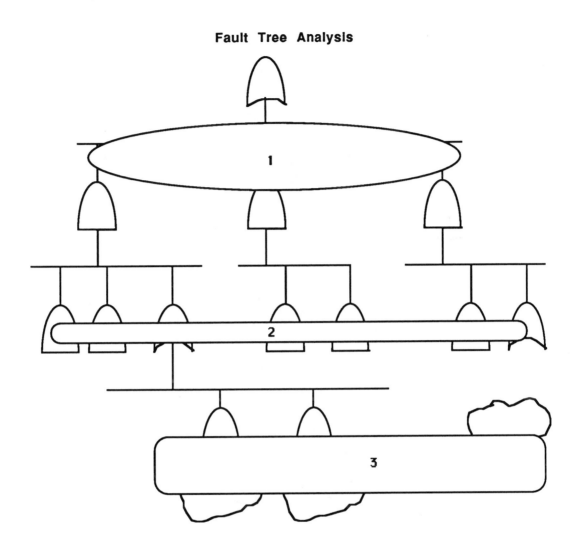

Figure 25.2 Instructions Chart F-2

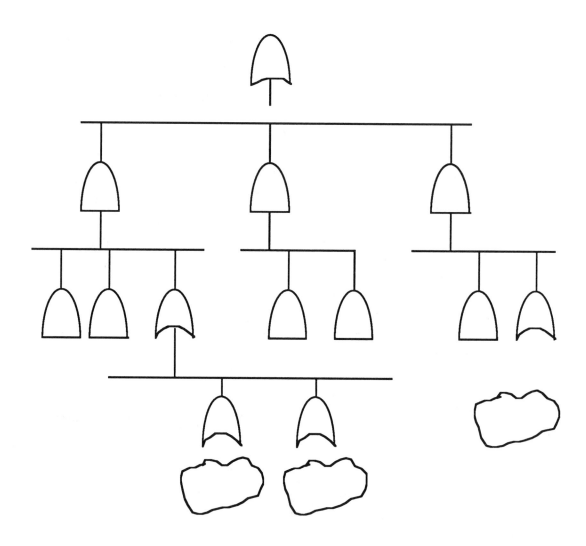

Figure 25.3 Practice Chart F-2

Chapter 26

Design Engineering Breakthroughs/ Reviewed Dendrograms, Factor Analysis

The Reviewed Dendrogram is the chart that orchestrates and records the work on engineering breakthroughs.

Description

The Reviewed Dendrogram is a kind of flow chart of investigation of breakthrough ideas. Each idea is examined with a set of questions and answers.

Purpose

The Reviewed Dendrogram documents the consideration of design breakthrough areas.

Summary

Inputs: ideas for improvement and criteria to evaluate them.

Background of the chart

A dendrogram is a tree-type classification used for large groups of information. For example, there is a dendrogram for the plant and mineral kingdom. There is a dendrogram for the animal kingdom including man. Man has the species <u>homo sapiens</u> in the vertibrate phyllum.

Kingdom	*Animal*
Phyllum	*Vertibrate*
Class	*Mammals*
Order	*Primates*
Family	*Hominidae*
Genus	*Homo*
Species	*sapiens*

The Reviewed Dendrogram lists ideas in a tree form and submits them to a set of criteria. The Reviewed Dendrogram was added to Quality Function Deployment in the mid-1980's.

Role in design

Sometimes the creative process is cut short in design when a possible solution is found. The RD provides a structure for a systematic consideration. It also documents what was considered and how it was disposed of. This is very important for later review in case of problems.

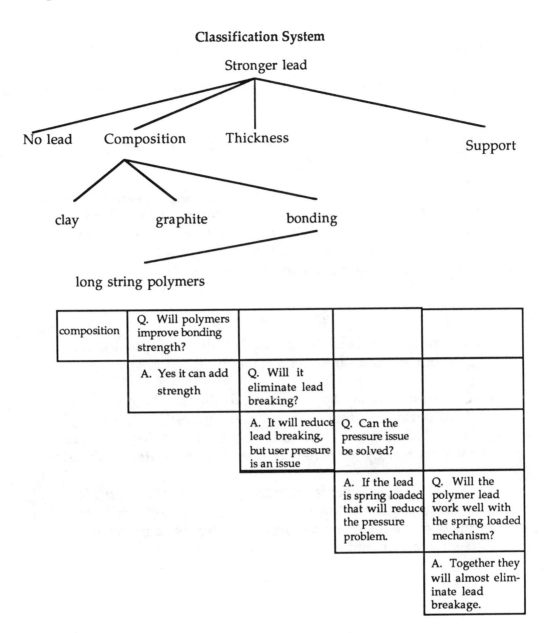

Figure 26.1 Pencil example Reviewed Dendrogram Chart F-3
(Bottleneck Engineering[1])

---

[1] Bottleneck Engineering is a concept promoted by Furukawa of the University of Hiroshima.

Instructions:

1. Map out a tree of possible solutions modeled after the dendrogram.

2. List breakthrough possibilities starting with any that appear more likely.

3. List criteria such as durability, cost, effectiveness. Ask whether each breakthrough possibility will meet the criteria and list under what conditions. Boxes are set up in a question and answer format. For example: "Will it cost more?", "No! It could cost less by combining parts a and b as one part".

4. Suggestions:

   a. Be sure to include in the criteria list all requirements, e.g., government and safety requirements.

   b. The questions may appear erratic at times. The reviewed dendrogram is a report of the minds investigation of breakthroughs and it will often be erratic. It does provide the opportunity for review at a later time for items missed.

   c. Oftentimes the reviewed dendrogram will raise issues for which there are no answers. This will lead to testing. In this case the reviewed dendrogram becomes a record of needed testing and results.

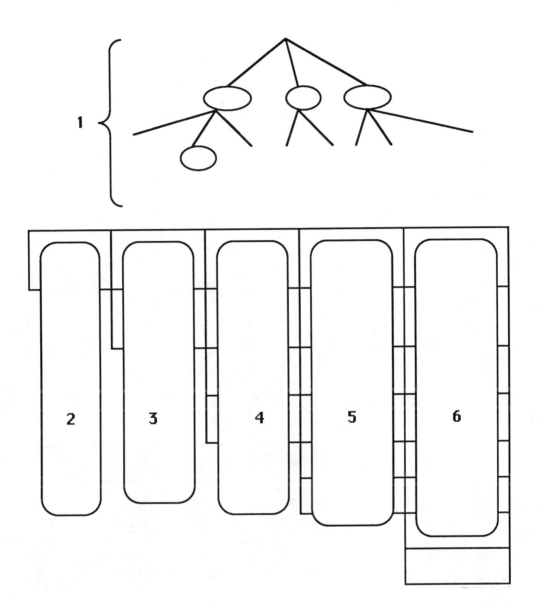

Figure 26.2 Instructions Chart F-3

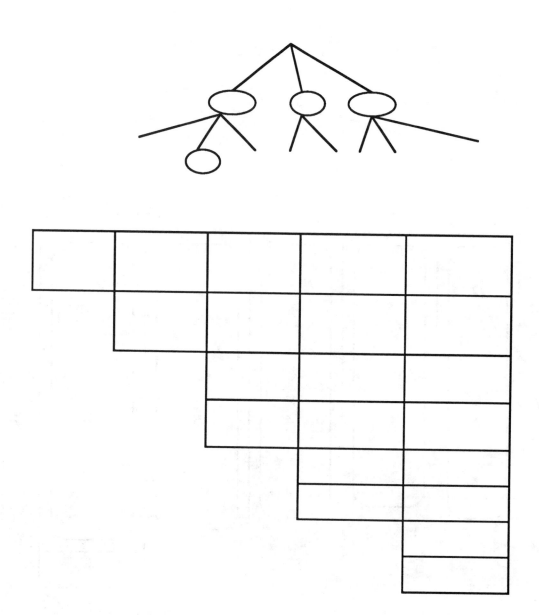

Figure 26.3 Practice Chart F-3

Factor Analysis

The reviewed dendrogram provides a list of things to find out. Sometimes this is accomplished by testing. It can also be accomplished by designed experiments. Though developed by R. Fisher in the 1920's, it wasn't until the mid 1980's that many organizations in the U.S. began to actively use this tool. Dr. Genichi Taguchi, with a controversial approach, awakened this sleeping giant of a friend. The American Supplier Institute is promoting the use of Taguchi's philosophy. GOAL/QPC offers a session in Taguchi applications during the Annual Conference in November.

Taguchi took Fisher's Factorial Designs and adopted them to engineering applications. Quality is defined by the amount of variation about the target value, the smaller the variance the higher the quality.   The impact of sources of variation is minimized by setting up experiments which intentionally create variation. The results are analyzed for factor levels which make the process or product insensitive to sources of variation.

A designed experiment using either Taguchi's Quality Engineering Concepts or the more classical approaches in books by G. Box; S. Hunter , B. Hunter; C. Hicks; F. Yates; W Cochran, or G. Cox have a similar message. You do not have to look at all combinations of factors to learn how to influence some quality characteristic.

For example the Chart A4 has the substitute quality characteristic "time between sharpening = 2.5 pages". What values of wood and lead satisfy the target of 2.5 pages? If there were more factors which are likely to impact the time between sharpening, the number of combinations goes up by the product of the number of levels used for each factor, i.e., two different woods, clays, graphites, binders, dyes, lubricants, and diameters. There are 128 combinations. Taguchi suggests that the experiment needs 8 trials while Box would suggest 16 or 32. Each of these trials could be performed by having several different people use the pencil on several different types of paper. The people and paper are intentional causes of variation. The results are analyzed in such a way as to both reduce the variation and attain the desired target without controlling the uncontrollable. A confirmation trial helps demonstrate that the predicted results actually work.

The Experiment would contain the following 8 combinations of factors:

Trial	Wood	Clay	Graphite	Binder	Dye	Lubricant	Diameter	Results
1	Oak	Red	Soft	Glue	Red	Oil	.5	1
2	Oak	Red	Soft	Epoxy	Black	Lard	.3	5
3	Oak	Blue	Hard	Glue	Red	Lard	.3	8
4	Oak	Blue	Hard	Epoxy	Black	Oil	.5	3
5	Cedar	Red	Hard	Glue	Black	Oil	.3	7
6	Cedar	Red	Hard	Epoxy	Red	Lard	.5	9
7	Cedar	Blue	Soft	Glue	Black	Lard	.5	0
8	Cedar	Blue	Soft	Epoxy	Red	Oil	.3	2

Figure 26.4

The effect of the two options of wood can be found by finding the average number of pages for the trials which used oak as well as the trials which used cedar.   Oak = $(1+5+8+3)/4 = 4.25$
Cedar = $(7+9+0+2)/4 = 4.5$

Probably not very important. However, look at graphite   Soft = $(1+5+0+2)/4 = 2.0$
Hard = $(8+3+7+9)/4 = 6.75$

There is definitely a difference in the two results.

For larger problems, or factors with different numbers of levels, or where interractions between factors are important there are many references available.

The results of the experiment would be parameter values for the parts to satisfy the quality characteristics. This same approach can be used in many of the QFD matrices.

As seen in Figure 26.4, the same type of control factors and quality characteristics are identified as are in the various matrices.[1]

---

[1]   The preceding two pages are contributed by John Terninko, Responsible Management Inc.

Taguchi Methods L8 Design Matrix

Trial Run	Factor						
	1	2	3	4	5	6	7
1	+1	+1	+1	+1	+1	+1	+1
2	+1	+1	+1	-1	-1	-1	-1
3	+1	-1	-1	+1	+1	-1	-1
4	+1	-1	-1	-1	-1	+1	+1
5	-1	+1	-1	+1	-1	+1	-1
6	-1	+1	-1	-1	+1	-1	+1
7	-1	-1	+1	+1	-1	-1	+1
8	-1	-1	+1	-1	+1	+1	-1

L8 Interaction Table

Column	1	2	3	4	5	6	7
	(1)	3	2	5	4	7	6
		(2)	1	6	7	4	5
			(3)	7	6	5	4
				(4)	1	2	3
					(5)	3	2
						(6)	1

Figure 26.5

These are the steps to use the interaction table:
1. Choose the lowest column number.
2. Find that number in parentheses along the diagonal.
3. Find the next number across the top of the table.
4. Move across the row and down the column until you intersect.
5. The number at the intersection is the interaction column.

<u>Some considerations for determining key factors through the use of</u> <u>Design of Experiments</u>

1.   The purpose of the experiment should be clearly defined. This definition should include objectives for the dependent variables.

2. The independent variables are brainstormed.

3. If there are not a lot of interactions it may be possible to use a fractional factorial experiment such as those popularized by Taguchi and the American Supplier Institute.

4. Calculate the total number of variables and interactions to be considered.

5.   Choose the smallest design matrix to accommodate the variables and interactions.

6.   Assign independent variables, interactions and remaining variables to columns, using the interactions table to get the interactions in the right column.

7. Ignore all columns with no variables.

8.   Replace the +1's with the high level of each respective variable. Replace the -1's with the low level for each respective variable.

9. Run the trials with special care for consistency.

10. Calculate the grand average of the response. Calculate the average response for the high level and low level of each variable.

11. Calculate the expected results under optimal conditions, that is, using the positive conditions, and under adverse conditions, that is; using all the adverse conditions.

12. Run the confirmation runs to see if the results are near what is expected.

13. Consider the results of the interactions in the experiment.

14. Run additional trials to focus in on more detail on key factors or in the case where confirmation runs show that not all key factors or interactions have been identified to get the results sought by the trial.

Many large volumes have been written on this subject by Taguchi [1] in Japan and by George Box and Stuart Hunter [2] among others in the United States. Those who are familiar with these ideas will hopefully see the tie-in between QFD and design of experiments. Those unfamiliar with design of experiments will need to explore it beyond what is possible here to understand its full significance.

---

[1]   Genichi Taguchi. *Introduction to Quality Engineering, Designing Quality into Products and Processes.* White Plains, New York, Kraus International Publications. (1986)

[2]   G.E.P. Box, W.G. Hunter, and J.S. Hunter (1978), *Statistics for Experimenters.* New York: John Wiley & Sons.

NOTES

Chapter 27

The Design Improvement Plan

Description of Chart F-4

Chart F-4 is a table that lists the parts costs, the estimate for parts, original targets such as cost and physical weight, and the number of the bottleneck engineering study (Reviewed Dendrograms--see previous pages). It lists the new design plan and the resulting cost, physical weight, etc. It concludes with identification of what parts are critical for function, subassembly and reliability.

Purpose of chart

To identify results as they relate to the design and the original design goals.

Summary

Inputs: parts, goals, plans

Outputs: results of design launch, parts in trial for function, subassembly and reliability

Background of the chart

The chart was developed in the mid-1980's to account for additions of reliability, cost and bottleneck engineering to the quality function deployment system.

Place in design engineering

This is a preliminary chart as one begins to prepare for manufacturing.

	goals		NE registration #	Plan							design		important considerations		
cost estimate	weight g.	cost		use long polymers	use plastic body	new eraser formulat.	cold formed spring	fool proof spring cap	spring loaded lead	pocket clip	g. weight	cost	parts critical for function	critical sub-assemblies	parts critical for reliability
lead				◎									◎		
body					◎				◎						
eraser						◎									
spring							◎	◎					◎		◎
spring cap									◎					◎	

Figure 27.1 Pencil example Chart F-4

Comments

1. The key design changes are listed: use of long polymers, use of plastic, new eraser formulation, cold formed spring, etc.

2. The chart also indicates which items are critical for function, subassembly and reliability.

Instructions for filling out Chart F-4

1. Identify cost estimate for critical parts.

2. Identify physical weight goal of part in grams
   (or other critical dimension for the study).

3. Identify cost goal for the part.

4. Identify the bottleneck engineering study number.

5. List the design items that have been developed to meet
   cost and weight goals.

6. List gram weight based on prototype tests.

7. List cost estimate based on prototype tests.

8. Identify parts critical to control for function or safety.

9. Identify assemblies critical to control for function or
   safety.

10. Identify parts important to control for reliability.

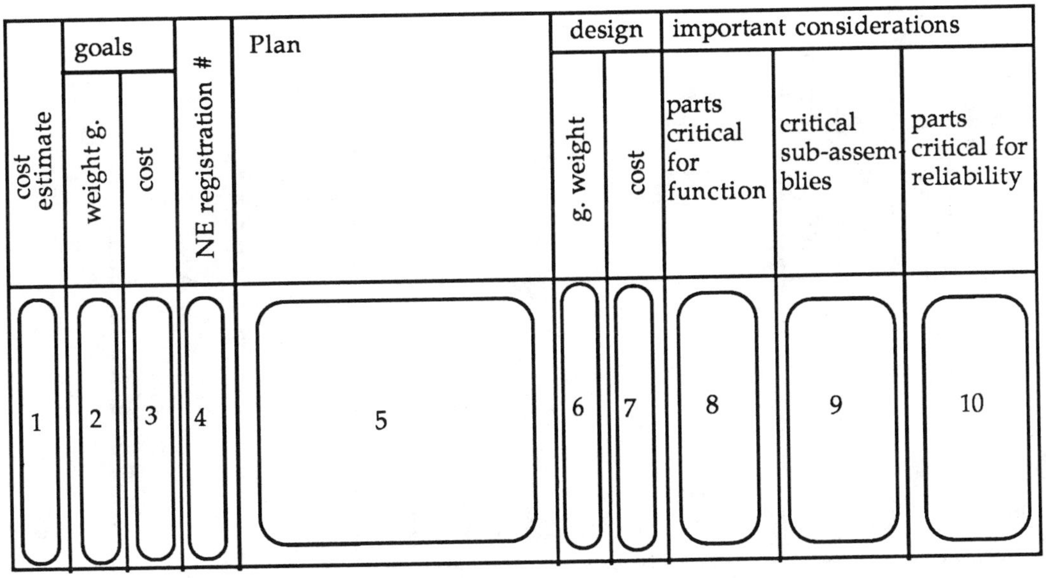

cost estimate	goals		NE registration #	Plan	design		important considerations		
	weight g.	cost			g. weight	cost	parts critical for function	critical sub-assemblies	parts critical for reliability
1	2	3	4	5	6	7	8	9	10

Figure 27.2 Instructions Chart F-4

cost estimate	goals		NE registration #	Plan	design		important considerations		
	weight g.	cost			g. weight	cost	parts critical for function	critical sub-assemblies	parts critical for reliability

Figure 27.3 Practice Chart F-4

Chapter 28

Chart G-1:   QA Table

The QA Table is the communication document between design and manufacturing.

Description

The QA Table lists the various parts, degree of importance, quality chart level (A-4), quality characteristics, design specifications, problems if design specifications are not met, and remarks.

Purpose of the table

To improve communication between design and manufacturing and to improve motivation for critical design items by identifying the problems if not satisfied.

Summary

Inputs: design quality requirements for initial parts and reasons for maintaining standards

Outputs: better parts

Background of the chart

The chart was developed in the mid-1970s to improve communication between design and manufacturing. It was later improved by adding the column "problems if not satisfied".

Its role in product design

In the past some companies have designed a product and thrown it over to manufacturing to see if they could make it. This chart, developed jointly by product design and manufacturing during the design phase, helps reduce some of those problems.

QA TABLE

Degree of Importance	Drawing Part Level	Part Name	Quality Chart Part#				Quality Characteristics	Quality Design	Problems if not satisified	Remarks
			1	2	3	4				
A	1	Spring					proper tension	spring recoil	lead will break	
A	6	pocket clip					clip formed correctly	proper mold	clip will break	
S	1	spring					end not sharp	end fits	cuts of assemblers	

Figure 28.1 Pencil example Chart G-1

Comments:

1. Some companies use the tree diagram to number parts using each level of the tree diagram as a separate digit.

Instructions for filling out Chart G-1

1. List whether critical for function or safety.

2. List drawing number.

3. List part.

4. List four digit part number from Chart B-2.

5. List quality characteristics.

6. List design specifications.

7. List problems if not satisfied.

8. List any special remarks or comments.

QA TABLE

Degree of Importance	Drawing Part Level	Part Name	Quality Chart Part#				Quality Characteristics	Quality Design	Problems if not satisified	Remarks
			1	2	3	4				
1	2	3.	4				5	6	7	8

Figure 28.2 Instructions Chart G-1

QA TABLE

Degree of Importance	Drawing Part Level	Part Name	Quality Chart Part# 1 2 3 4	Quality Characteristics	Quality Design	Problems if not satisified	Remarks

Figure 28.3 Practice Chart G-1

Chapter 29

Chart G-2   Equipment Deployment

This is the Purchasing Chart that tells where the parts are coming from and why.

Description of the chart

This chart lists the various production options and compares each supplier in-house or out in terms of cost and quality.

Purpose of the chart

The chart determines which is the best equipment to produce the part in terms of quality and cost.

Summary

Inputs: information on various options' cost and quality

Outputs: decision on best supplier

Background of the chart

The chart was developed in the 1960's to choose better suppliers and was added to the QFD system in the mid-1970's.

Its role in product design

This chart involves the purchasing and manufacturing people in the design process.

Parts Spring for Pencil

G-2		obtain steel	form wire	coil wire	cut spring	inspect spring	Totals
Supplier A	Off Quality	5%	3%	5%	3%	10%	
	Cost	20	4	5	2	1	32
Supplier B	Off Quality	20%	15%	10%	6%	25%	
	Cost	8	8	10	3	2	31
Supplier C	Off Quality	0	0	0	0	no inspection	
	Cost	10	2	3	1	0	16

Legend: All quality in % defective; all costs in .001 cents per unit

Figure 29.1 Pencil example Chart G-2[1]

Note: "supplier" may refer also to goods produced in-house rather than purchased to compare make vs. buy.

---

[1] Other possible supplier measures include: cp/cpk, on time delivery. shipping cost, service, traceability, technology cycle time, quality sytems, cycle cost.

Instructions for filling out Chart G-2

      1. List critical parts.

      2. List quality Supplier A.

      3. List cost, Cpk, accuracy at Supplier A.

      4. List quality at Supplier B.

      5. List cost, Cpk, accuracy at Supplier B.

      6. List quality at Supplier C.

      7. List cost, Cpk, and accuracy at Supplier C.

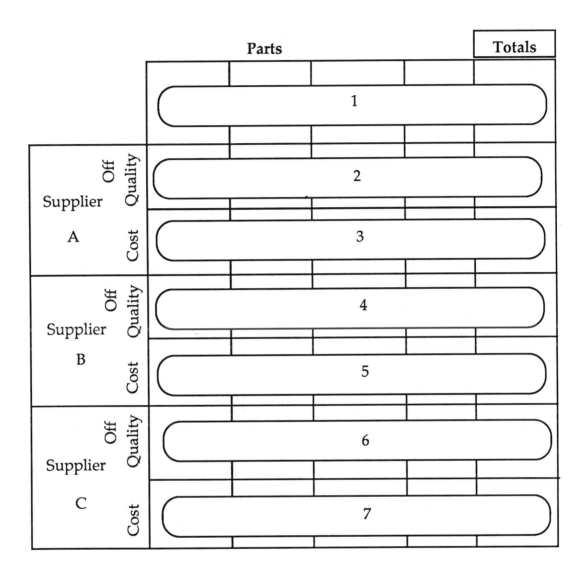

Figure 29.2 Instruction Chart G-2

		Parts				Totals
Supplier A	Off Quality					
	Cost					
Supplier B	Off Quality					
	Cost					
Supplier C	Off Quality					
	Cost					

Figure 29.3 Practice Chart G-2

Chapter 30

Chart G-3:   Process Planning

Description

This chart lists the process number, the process name, the conditions of manufacturing, including equipment and indexing parts characteristics and central points in the process.

Purpose

The purpose is to begin to identify how the process will be controlled.

Summary

Inputs: process parts characteristics

Outputs: control points of processes

<u>Background of the chart</u>

The chart was developed during the mid-1970's to plan on how to control processes during the manufacturing of initial parts.

<u>Role in design</u>

This chart brings together the process and design engineers. It is a kind of simultaneous engineering in the narrow sense.

Example
G-3

Chart G3 Process Planning Chart

No.	Process	Conditions of Manufacturing		Parts Characteristics	Control points of Process
		Equipment	Index		
1	obtain steel			freedom from rust	incoming observation
2	form wire	extruder		diameter flex	O.D. Dimension degree of flex
3	coil wire	coiler		tension	amount of spring level of recoil
4	cut spring	crimp		smooth	degree of smoothness

1

Figure 30. 1 Pencil example Chart G-3

---

[1] Machine settings or cp/cpk are put in this column.

Instructions for filling out Chart G-3

1. List part #.

2. List process.

3. List equipment.

4. List settings.

5. List parts characteristics.

6. List critical points of process for special control.

Q.C. Process Planning Chart

No.	Process	Conditions of Manufacturing		Parts Characteristics	Control points of Process
		Equipment	Index		
1	2	3	4	5	6

Figure 30.2 Instruction Chart G-3

Chapter 30   Chart G-3   Q.C. Process Planning Chart

No.	Process	Conditions of Manufacturing		Parts Characteristics	Control points of Process
		Equipment	Index		

Figure 30.3 Practice Chart G-3

Chapter 31

Chart G-4   Process Fault Tree Analysis

Description

This chart is a Fault Tree Analysis of the process. It lists the general ways in which a process can fail and then some of the causes and sub-causes. It goes from the symptoms of problems to the real root causes.

Purpose

To determine root causes of failures.

Summary

Inputs: kinds of failures

Outputs: focused picture of causes of failure at various levels

Background of the chart

The Fault Tree Analysis goes back at least to the 1960's. It was added to the QFD system in the late 1970's.

Role in design

This chart makes process planning more reliable and focuses processes reliability work by indicating the interrelationships among failure modes.

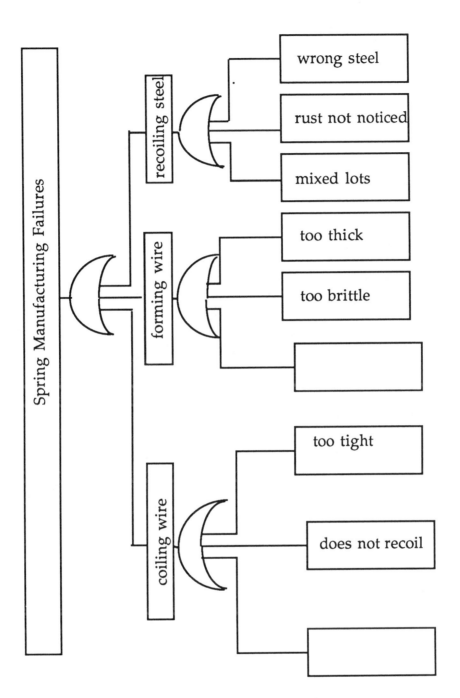

Figure 31.1 Pencil example Chart G-4

Instructions

1. Brainstorm the potential process failure modes, write on cards, rearrange the cards so they form a tree going from general to specific.

2. Use ⌂ for "and" and ⌂ for "or".

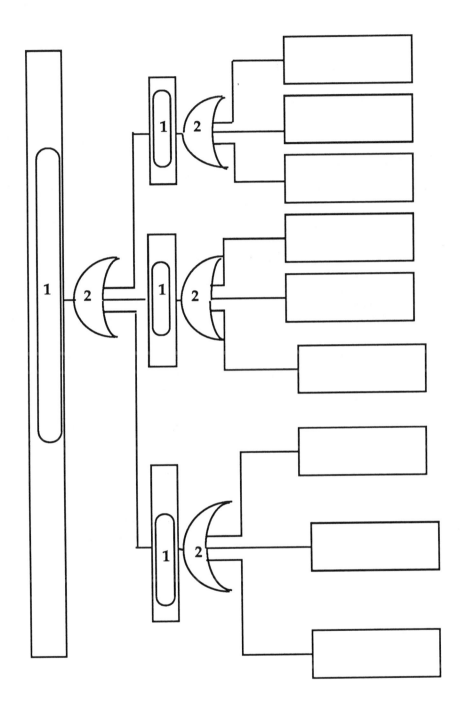

Figure 31.2 Instruction Chart G-4

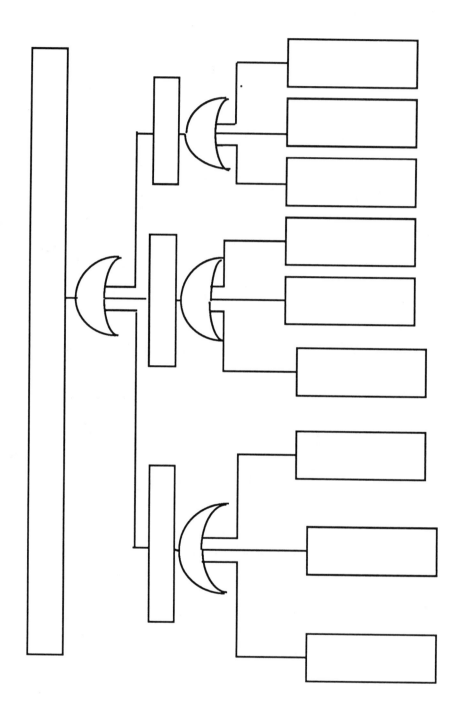

Figure 31.3 Practice Chart G-4

Chapter 32

Chart G-5   Process FMEA

Description

Chart G-5 identifies the various ways the process can fail, ranks these ways with a risk priority number, identifies corrective actions and resulting improvement in risk priority number. Looking at it in more detail, Chart G-5 lists the various parts processes, potential failure modes, potential effects of failures, potential causes of failures, initial controls, and conditions contributing to the risk priority number. These conditions include the likelihood of the failure taking place (occurrence), the damage if it happens (severity) and the likelihood that it will be discovered before the product gets to the customer (detection). It concludes with responsible activity.

Purpose

Chart G-5 provides a systematic way to consider potential failure modes. It enables the prioritization of potential failures. Coupled with process fault tree analysis (Chart G-4), it provides a sound strategy for reliable processes.

Summary

inputs: failure mode information
outputs: corrective action information

Background of the chart

This chart has been widely used both in the U.S. and Japan. There is some variation from company to company of the details included in the chart. The format used here is that developed by Ford Motor Company and required of their suppliers.

Role in design engineering

This chart prioritizes the reliability engineering for process design.

Process Failure Mode and Effect Analysis

Process _ *Spring forming*   Outside Suppliers Affected_   *B &E Spring machine*

Process Responsibility_   *Paul King*   Model Year_   *1988*   Engineer   *Bob King*   Supervisor   *Q. Public*

Scheduled Production Release_   *12/15/87*   Initial Date   *6/15/87*   Revisions   *12/9/87*

Part Name/ Number	Process Function	Potential Failure Mode	Potential Effects of Failure	Safety	Potential Cause of Failure(s)	Existing Conditions				Risk Priority#	Recommended Actions and Status	Resulting					Responsible Activity
						Current Controls	Occurance	Severity	Detection			Actions Taken	Occurance	Severity	Detection	RPN	
spring	*support lead* *prevent breaking*	*looses recoil*	*lead breaks*		*cooling too quickly* *uneven diameter*	*visual check*	7	6	8	336	*slower cooling* *spring test by operator*	*slowed cooling* *self inspection*	3	6	3	54	R.N.King

Figure 32.1 Pencil example Chart G-5

<u>Instructions</u>

1. Name operation being studied.

2. Name unit responsible for process.

3. List suppliers of parts for process.

4. List model year.

5. List date component, sub-system or system will be turned over to production.

6. Name of engineer filling out form.

7. Name of managing supervisor.

8. Date when first edition of chart was done.

9. Date(s) of chart revisions.

10. Identify part(s) name(s) and number(s).

11. List part functions.

12. List potential failure modes from FTA (Chart G-3).

13. List potential effects, i.e., indicators of failure.

14. Place an inverted Δ or other symbol to indicate a safety item or government safety regulation.

15. List potential causes of failure.

16. List procedures or other controls used to prevent or detect failure.

17. List likelihood of failure happening on a scale of 1-10, e.g., 1 being remote (1/10,000), 3 being low (1/2,000), 5 being moderate (1/500), 7 being high (1/100), 10 being very high (1/10 +).

Process Failure Mode and Effect Analysis

Process ___①___   Outside Suppliers Affected___③_____
Process Responsibility___②___   Model Year___④___   Engineer___⑥___Supervisor___⑦___
                              Scheduled Production Release___⑤___   Initial Date ___⑧___ Revisions___⑨___

Part Name/ Number	Process Function	Potential Failure Mode	Potential Effects of Failure	Safety	Potential Cause of Failure(s)	Existing Conditions				Risk Priority#	Recommended Actions and Status	Resulting					Responsible Activity
						Current Controls	Occurence	Severity	Detection			Actions Taken	Occurence	Severity	Detection	RPN	
⑩	⑪	⑫	⑬	⑭	⑮	⑯	⑰	⑱	⑲	⑳	㉑	㉒	23				㉔

Figure 32.2 Instruction Chart G-5

18. List seriousness of effect if it happens on a scale of 1-10, e.g., 1 indicates no noticeable effect, 3 indicates slight customer dissatisfaction, 5 indicates some customer dissatisfaction and annoyance, 7 indicates product or part is inoperable, 10 indicates a safety problem or noncompliance with a government regulation.

19. Estimate probability of product getting out without detecting a defect, e.g.:
1 indicates remote likelihood of shipping with defect
        (1/10,000);
3 indicates low likelihood of shipping with defect (1/2000);
6 indicates moderate likelihood of shipping with defect
        (1/200);
9 indicates high likelihood of shipping with defect (1/20+).

20. Risk priority number is the product of item 17 x item 18 x item 19.

21. List recommendations for concrete actions that will significantly improve the situation.

22. Actions that made the difference.

23. New index numbers formulated as in items 17,18,19,20.

24. Person responsible for the new approach.

Process Failure Mode and Effect Analysis

Process _____   Outside Suppliers Affected_____
Process Responsibility_____   Model Year_____   Engineer_____Supervisor_____
                              Scheduled Production Release_____   Initial Date _____ Revisions_____

Part Name/ Number	Process Function	Potential Failure Mode	Potential Effects of Failure	Safety	Potential Cause of Failure(s)	Existing Conditions				Risk Priority#	Recommended Actions and Status	Resulting					Responsible Activity
						Current Controls	Occurence	Severity	Detection			Actions Taken	Occurence	Severity	Detection	RFN	

Figure 32.3 Practice Chart G-5

Chapter 33

Chart G-6 QC Process Chart for Parts & Assembly

Description

This table lists the details of·how the process will be controlled and the quality assured. It lists process number and name, machines for manufacturing process, quality check items and standards, methods of control (e.g., control limit criteria), measuring instruments, sample size, etc. It delineates how and where information will be recorded. It identifies who will take action if the process is out of control.

Purpose

The chart describes process and quality controls in detail.

Summary

Inputs: process and quality requirements

Outputs: details in control

Background

This chart was developed in the mid-1970's as part of QFD manufacturing deployment. It has become quite popular in the 1980's because many Japanese companies in the U.S. and Japan require it of their suppliers with all incoming products. It is probably the most widely used of all QFD charts.

Role in design

This is the chart that gives the detailed overview of how processes and quality will be controlled--the heart of manufacturing deployment.

Q.C. Process Chart

Dept Name/# QFD/ 101	section head Y. Akao
date prepared 7/15/87	preparer Bob King
revisions 12/19/87	.

Part Name/ Number	Flow chart		process name	work instruction sheet #	process control item	Control Method							Inspection item	Inspection method					
	raw material	process				person in charge	place	when	measure-ment	sampling method	standard	control data		person in charge	sensory data	instruction sheet #	sampling method	record kept	in charge of action
spring	1		obtain steel																
	▽		store steel	102	lot #'s	a	ware-house K	1 mo.	count	100%	zero defects	check sheet	rust	c	see	--		log sheet	e
	○3		form wire																
	○4		coil wire	104	temperature	e	coiler 6	every 20 min	temp. guage	once 30 min.	F degrees	control chart	spring tension	d	feel	tension testor	5 every 20 min.	control chart	f
	○5		cut spring																
	◇6		inspection																

Figure 33.1 Pencil Example Chart G-6

Instructions

1. Identify production department name and number.

2. Identify section head responsible for department.

3. Identify date QC process chart was prepared.

4. List dates of revisions.

5. List person(s) who prepared chart and revisions.

6. Identify part(s) name(s) and number(s).

7. Indicate place of raw materials in a flow chart.

8. Indicate place of processes in a flow chart.

9. Identify process names.

10. Identify number of work instruction sheet for the process.

11. List process items to be controlled.

12. Identify person in charge of process.

13. Identify where process is controlled.

14. Identify when process is checked.

15. Identify what measurement is taken.

16. Identify sampling method used (if applicable).

17. List control standards.

18. List form where data is recorded.

19. List items inspected.

Q.C. Process Chart

Dept Name/# ①	section head ②
date prepared ③ revisions ④	preparer ⑤

Part Name/ Number	Flow chart		process name	work instruction sheet #	process control item	Control Method							Inspection item	Inspection method						
	raw mat'l	process				person in charge	place	when	measure-ment	sampling method	standard	control data		person in charge	sensory data	instruction sheet #	tool	sampling method	record kept	in charge of action
⑥	⑦	⑧	⑨	⑩	⑪	⑫	⑬	⑭	⑮	⑯	⑰	⑱	⑲	⑳	㉑	㉒	㉓	㉔	㉕	㉖

Figure 33.2　Instruction Chart G-6

20.　Identify person who does the inspection.

21.　Identify what kind of sensory data is used.

22.　Identify inspection instruction sheet number.

23.　Identify sampling method (if applicable).

24.　Identify form where data is recorded.

25.　Identify person in charge of taking action.

Q.C. Process Chart

Dept Name/#	section head
date prepared revisions	prepider

Flow chart		process name	work instruction sheet #	process control item	Control Method						Inspection item	Inspection method						
Part Name Number	raw material	process				person in charge	place	when	measure- ment	sampling method	standard	control data		person in charge	sensory data	instruction sheet #	sampling method	record kept	in charge of action

Figure 33.3 practice Chart G-6

Chapter 34

QFD Implementation

In 1975, Kayaba, Japan's premier producer of shock absorbers decided to implement QFD. They went to one of their customers, Toyota, who was already experienced in QFD and asked for sample charts and instructions. Toyota cooperated fully and gave Kayaba the forms. Kayaba went to work filling out the charts. The effort was almost a total failure. What Kayaba learned from this experience was that since they were a different company from Toyota, they needed to develop their own charts and QFD system customized to their needs. This they did, and in 1980 they won the Deming prize for their implementation of Total Quality Control with special recognition for their QFD, which they called by the term "anticipatory development."

Kayaba had learned the important lesson that QFD charts and systems should not be copied. Once the principles are understood, then charts need to be customized to an individual operation. The charts in this book are models to use to learn the principles of QFD. Introducing QFD will mean a fundamental change for many organizations in the way they design their products. Most companies go through two phases. The first phase is individual projects using one or more charts. The second phase, which usually starts after three years, is changing the design system. Since all U.S. companies are still in phase one, this chapter will deal with what charts people are using in pilot projects and what kind of success and difficulty they are having. Those interested in system change are directed to courses, books and articles on Management by Policy (MBP - Hoshin Kanri in Japanese).[1]

---

[1] GOAL/QPC has a two day course in Management By Planning, Hoshin Kanri, and is developing a textbook.

Research on QFD usage

Toward the end of 1986, Yoji Akao, chairman of the QFD research committee of the Japan Society for Quality Control, conducted a survey of QFD usage among the larger member companies of the Union of Japanese Scientists and Engineers (J.U.S.E.). [2] The study showed that although QFD was not being used in some Japanese companies, it had grown significantly, and was used extensively and with great success at many Japanese companies.

The following section reviews some of the results in Japan and compares them with the experience of American companies.

Companies using QFD
  In Japan

Of 148 J.U.S.E. member companies who were surveyed, 148 responded. Of those, 80 use QFD and 68 do not. Of the 68 who do not, 16 have won the Deming Prize.

industry / answer	electronics	precision machines	transportation	process industry	metal steel	construction	other manu- facturing	service	total
yes	24	14	13	10	1	9	2	7	80
no	14	7	2	15	2	2	11	15	68
number of replies	38	21	15	25	3	11	13	22	148

[3] Figure 34.1 Results of JSQC Question: Do You Use QFD?

---

[2]   Proceedings of ICQC '87 - Tokyo, B-1-02.
[3] Eight companies who are not using QFD are in the process of preparation to use QFD.

In the U.S.

As of the end of 1987, many U.S. industries have begun to use QFD.

Automotive　Ford, General Motors and Chrysler are heavy users of QFD themselves and are urging their suppliers to get started. GM has completed two whole vehicle studies and the cars will be on the road by 1991. Ford Climate Control has done studies with many suppliers, Cirtek and Buehler to name a couple. Other suppliers with numerous projects include Masland, Rockwell International and Sheller Globe.

Electronics　Digital and Texas Instruments have been QFD leaders in the electronic field. But AT&T Bell Labs and Hewlett Packard also have numerous QFD projects underway. The 3M company has been using QFD in their floppy disk division since 1984.

Other companies with a large number of projects include Procter and Gamble, Kendall Company and Omark Industries in their tree harvesting divisions. Companies gearing up for 1988 QFD projects include John Deere and General Electric.

Results of Using QFD
In Japan

Design time was reduced by 1/3 to 1/2 in companies using QFD in Japan. Other benefits included:
1. Setting design quality became easier.
2. Problems with initial quality decreased.
3. Setting planning quality became easier.
4. Comparison with competitors' products and analysis was made possible.
5. Control points on the job were clarified.
6. Solidarity between divisions improved.
7. Design aim was able to be communicated to manu-facturing.[4]

4　JSQC Survey Table 6.　Question 16.　Full survey summary results are available from GOAL/QPC, 13 Branch St., Methuen, MA., 01844.

<u>In the United States</u>

It is still too early to have many success stories to tell in the States because QFD is so new. Omark Industries and 3M have been using QFD since 1984 and have numerous product improvements based on QFD. A major consumer products company has reported a 500% increase in sales in one division based partially on use of the QFD method.[5] Digital's new VAX system released in 1988 also benefited from use of QFD. Buehler has developed a new product for Ford Climate Control. Documentation shows that it was a superior product and designed in one half the time (as measured by total engineering hours) compared with other similar products they have designed. [6]

Dramatic improvements in market share and significant reductions in design time are good calling cards for QFD. But there are also other benefits. Dave Taylor, president of Cirtek, a one hundred employee Michigan electronics firm, also reports:

1. Better understanding of customer needs through use of affinity diagram.
2. Improved organization on development projects.
3. Improved organization while putting a product into production.
4. Decreased amount of design changes late in development.
5. Commitment from the customer toward finalization of the design.
6. Fewer manufacturing problems at start up.
7. Reputation for being serious about quality.
8. Increased business due to all of the above. [7]

<u>Which charts do people use?</u>
<u>In Japan</u>

The A-1 chart, customer demands vs. substitute quality characteristics, is the most widely used, but over 80 other kinds of QFD matrices are documented in the JSQC survey.

---

[5]   As reported at GOAL/QPC Annual; conference, November, 1987.

[6]   As reported at GOAL/QPC Annual Conference, Plymouth, MA, 1987.

[7]   Ibid.

It is clear that companies who have been using QFD for some time have been expanding their usage. Over half of companies responding to the JSQC survey are using QFD in conjunction with technology deployment (59%) and reliability deployment (53%). And over one third of those responding are using QFD with Cost Deployment (43%).

Demanded Quality	Quality Characteristics	reliability deployment	function deployment	cost deployment	component deployment	component material	raw material	operations	engineering	mechanism	process method	process deployment	other	Types of deployment
23	*128	29	46	22	19	13	10	5	22	7	9	12	13	Demanded Quality
	11	16	32	4	38	6	6	1	22	16	11	20	6	Quality Characteristics
		6	15	2	21	3	3	3	11	7	1	5	5	reliability deployment
			6	7	14	5	1	0	12	11	2	10	1	function deployment
				4	15	5	4	2	4	4	5	5	1	cost deployment
					1	5	2	2	11	5	5	3	1	component deployment
						0	2	1	2	2	2	2	1	component material
							0	2	2	0	0	1	0	raw material
								1	1	0	0	0	0	operations
									1	4	3	4	3	engineering
										0	4	2	0	mechanism
											0	0	1	process method
												0	1	process deployment
													0	other

Figure 34.2 JSQC Question 25: What matrix of deployment was used?

* To understand this chart, consider that the items on top are on the top of the chart and the items on the side of the chart are on the side of the chart.

In the United States

Generally people in the United States are stuck on Chart A-1. There are several reasons for this:

1. Chart A-1 tells you a lot so it is valuable by itself.

2. Many companies are doing large charts 100 x 100 items or 10,000 possible correlations -- thus making it very time consuming.
3. Because of large charts for A-1, many do not have the energy or interest to go on to other charts.
4. Because QFD is relatively new, people are afraid to make a mistake and so keep working on Chart A-1.
5. Some are concerned that because of lack of good customer information, results of Chart A-1 may be incorrect so they are reluctant to take wrong conclusions of Chart A-1 to other charts.

Fortunately some are using other charts. GM Saturn is using QFD in conjunction with reliability engineering and Stuart Pugh's new concept selection with great benefit. The Keokuk, Iowa, plant of Sheller Globe uses all charts covered in this book. This effort has made it possible for them to change some errors in existing designs before the products went into production. Most GOAL/QPC QFD course participants report that when they are required to try all the charts it helps them understand what kind of information belongs on Chart A-1.

Who in the company is doing QFD?
In Japan

It is surprising that in many companies it is one person or only a few who are doing all the QFD work. In Japan where many companies tend to promote by seniority, QFD has become in some cases the means for energetic engineers to get ahead of their class by doing QFD charts by themselves on Saturdays.

In the United States

In most U. S. companies, sections of the company that have a critical interface are often the first to use QFD. At Procter and Gamble, the paper products division is using QFD to improve communications between process engineers and production supervisors/technicians. At Ford Light Truck, QFD has improved communication among engineering groups. For example, a project to improve tire wear brought together suspension, steering and tire engineers. The project improved definition of terms and integration of engineering concepts. For Masland, a new product development team including project manager, design, marketing and quality assurance used QFD to develop a new hood liner for an automobile. At Digital

Equipment Corporation initial QFD efforts were undertaken by the quality staff group of a design engineering group.

How long have people been using QFD?
In Japan

A major book on QFD was released in Japan in 1978 and that led to an increased use of QFD in the early 1980's.

year	first tried QFD	QFD system used
1969	1	0
1970	2	1
1971	0	0
1972	3	0
1973	1	1
1974	1	0
1975	2	1
1976	1	1
1977	1	0
1978	5	2
1979	4	1
1980	6	3
1981	11	6
1982	8	7
1983	11	6
1984	9	11
1985	7	6
1986	2	3
	-------	-------
	75	49

Figure 34.3 JSQC Question 4: When did you first use QFD?

Question 7: When was QFD used as a system?

In the United States

There has not yet been a formal survey in the U.S., but the author knows personally of two companies in the U.S who started QFD in 1984, ten in 1986 and fifteen in 1987.

Reasons why people have not started QFD
In Japan

Most companies in Japan report they have not tried QFD because they do not know how. Reasons given in the JSQC survey include the following:

1. Do not know how to apply (35%).
2. Do not know how to deploy (34%).
3. There is no example of business similar to ours (24%).
4. No good text available (22%).
5. Cannot understand demanded quality (13%).
6. Do not have good communication among divisions (12%).
7. In the process of studying and preparing for application (12%).

Figure 34.4 JSQC Question 28: What are the reasons for your not using QFD?

In the United States

Yoji Akao first introduced QFD in the U. S. in an article in the October 1983 issue of Quality Progress, the monthly publication of the American Society for Quality Control. In November, 1983, the Cambridge Corporation of Tokyo, under the leadership of Masaaki Imai, conducted a TQC and QFD workshop in Chicago. Most of the people who attended were not from top management and only a few used the opportunity to begin implementing QFD. GOAL/QPC offered one day courses in QFD in 1984 and 1985. With the introduction of Akao's materials into GOAL's five day QFD courses in February of 1986 and Akao's personal involvement in 1986, QFD began to spread quickly.

Larry Sullivan and John McHugh were instrumental initially in setting up QFD projects involving Ford Body and Assembly and its suppliers during 1985. Their work at the American Supplier Institute in Dearborn, Michigan in 1986 and 1987 provided extensive training in QFD to automotive companies, their suppliers and other industries as well.

What problems did people have in applying QFD?

In Japan

One of the biggest problems mentioned was people had trouble understanding the customer.

1. Quality chart becomes too big (67%).
2. Demanded quality is hard to understand (54%).
3. Sensory content is hard to put into demanded quality chart (54%).
4. Cannot judge if customer-demanded quality understanding is appropriate or not (46%).
5. Users' information is hard to collect (40%).
6. Degree of relation is hard to rate ((0), O, $\triangle$).
7. Hard to classify into primary, secondary, and so forth (28%).

Figure 34.6 Results of JSQC Question 17:
          What problems did you have applying QFD?

In the United States

Some of the problems encountered in the U.S. include:
    1. In some cases people tried to start with a brand new product that no one had made. In this case it was too hard to identify customer demands.

    2. Because design and other departments are not used to working as a team, there were often some communication problems. These were solved by beginning to define terms.

    3. Lack of good customer information slowed down the process in cases where people had to interrupt the process to do surveys and focus groups.

    4. The problems identified in the JSQC study are also common in many initial U.S. projects.

    5. In some cases where customers have pushed their suppliers to do QFD, excessive unwanted paperwork has soured people on QFD.

6. Failure to reduce chart size has led to too much time on QFD and a poor cost/benefit ratio for QFD.

7. Some QFD projects have been completed too late to make changes in a particular product, thus leading to frustration.

In conclusion, QFD seems to be developing more quickly in the U.S. than in Japan. It involves a lot of up front work. Those who have stuck with it are claiming incredible payoffs.

What principles can be learned from preliminary experience with QFD in the U.S.?

1. Plan on two or three years of experience with QFD projects before trying to change the design system.

2. One of the first projects should be to take an existing product or service and fill out charts (as a way to understand and "own" QFD).

3. Focus on projects which will improve key interfaces between departments. QFD, like other tools, works best when the focus is problem-oriented and not tool-oriented. In other words, the question is not "Where can I use QFD?" but "Which aspects of QFD will help me solve this or that problem?"

4. Participants in initial projects who are interested in QFD and want it to work will enhance the likelihood of its success.

5. Time and size reducing suggestions as spelled out in chapter four will help establish a good cost/benefit ratio early.

6. Early use of a variety of QFD charts will help determine what items are customer demands, functions, parts, specifications, reliability and other categories of information.

Appendix A

Affordable Innovation Using the Full Power of QFD's

Matrix of Matrices to Get Timely, Cost Effective,

Customer-Focused, Innovative Designs

Abstract

Quality Function Deployment is a cross-functional tool which enables organizations to prioritize customer demands, develop innovative responses which are reliable and cost effective, and orchestrate a successful implementation involving all departments. This paper offers some models of what QFD charts can be used during advanced design, project definition, detailed design, prototype and test, and continuous improvement after the product or service is being produced or delivered.

IMPORTANT NOTE: This is an initial approach to think about the systematization of QFD. It may not make sense until one has 6 - 12 months experience implementing QFD.

Introduction

Quality Function Deployment (QFD) is a cross-functional tool which enables organizations to prioritize customer demands, develop innovative responses to those needs, which is reliable and cost effective, and orchestrates a successful implementation involving all departments from marketing, research, design, manufacturing, QA, purchasing, sales and service, etc. If an organization fails to prioritize, fails to innovate, or if the new approach is not reliable or cost effective, or if it is bungled by any particular department or stage of development, then the QFD has been incomplete or defective.

QFD is part of Total Quality Management. Total Quality Management is a set of systems, organizations and tools in which all employees in all departments everyday maintain or improve quality, cost, procedures and systems to give customers a product which is best qualified, most economic and most useful. There are many methods that are helpful in achieving this. Some of the more important ones are illustrated in the following chart.

QFD is a sub-system of Quality Assurance which is at the core of the quality piece of cross-functional management. There are a number of important interactions in Total Quality Control. Some of them are reflected as follows:

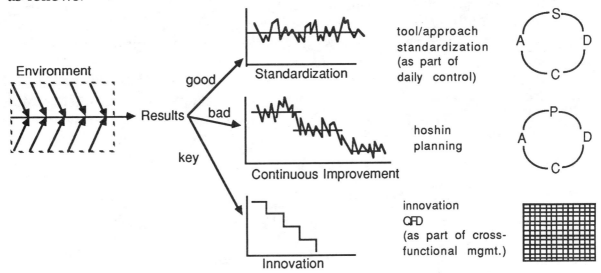

The purpose of this paper is to focus on QFD as a methodology for targeting and orchestrating cost effective innovation.

QFD Options/Strengths and Weaknesses

There are a couple of different approaches to QFD. One is more focused and one is more generic.

<u>Focused Approach</u> (Makabe/Clausing)

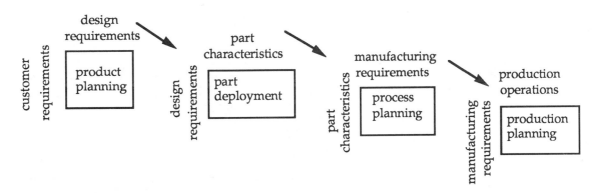

<u>Don Clausing and John Hauser</u>
       <u>As reported in the Harvard Business Review</u>

This approach is a modification of the QFD method used by Makabe to assist him in his reliability engineering consulting practice. Its value is its traceability from customer to manufacturing. It is very good for certain parts and components, but it is awkward for computers, automobiles and other complex systems. It is good for minor improvements in existing technology, but is not well suited for cost effective innovation. Makabe taught this approach to Fuji Xerox, who taught it to Don Clausing (formerly of Xerox), who taught it to ASI staff members and so it has come to be a major focus of the American Supplier Institute to Quality Function Deployment.

A more generic approach was developed by Yoji Akao in the mid 1980's. Its value was that it included linkages with value engineering and reliability charts such as FMEA, FTA, etc. This was adapted by the author to include new concept selection and other enhancements:

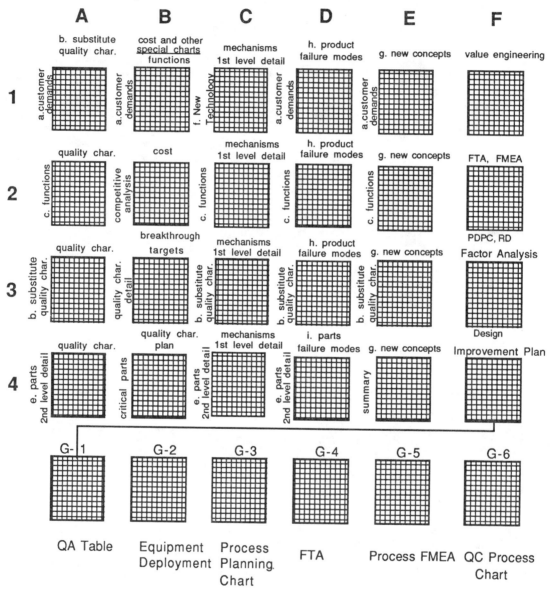

This matrix of matrices has the benefit of providing a number of different formats for QFD matrices. Its major weakness, in addition to its apparent complexity at first glance, is its lack of clear implementation steps.

An initial effort to solve this need for sequential direction was attempted by this arrow diagram:

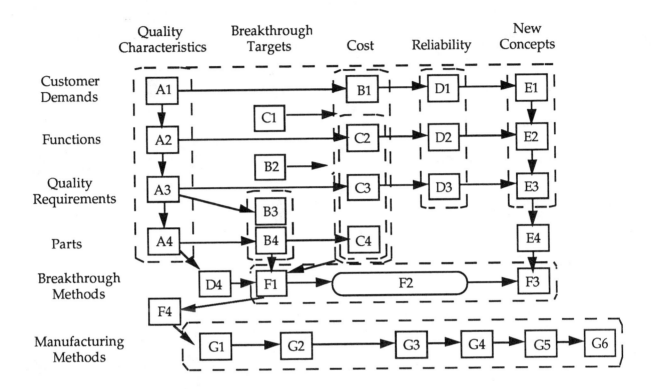

Purpose to be achieved	Charts to Use
Analyze customer demands	A1, B1, D1, E1
Critique functions	A2, C2, D2, E2
Set quality characteristics	A1, A2, A3, A4, B3, B4, C3, D3, E3
Identify critical parts	A4, B4, C4, E4
Set breakthrough targets	C1, B2, B3, B4
Set cost targets	B1, C2, C3, C4
Set reliability targets	D1, D2, D3, D4
Select new concepts	E1, E2, E3, E4
Identify breakthrough methods	D4, F1, F2, F3
Identify manufacturing methods	G1, G2, G3, G4, G5, G6

This chart shows not only which charts must be completed first but also in conjunction with the legend identifies the general purpose of each chart, thus encouraging the reader to be problem focused rather than tool focused. The disadvantage of this chart is that it suggests that the charts are static where in effect they are iterative.

Another attempt to sequence the chart is represented by the following chart:

Design Steps

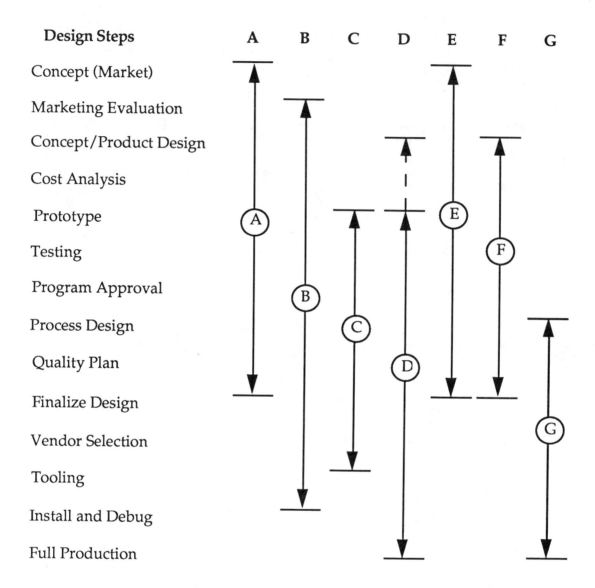

Concept (Market)

Marketing Evaluation

Concept/Product Design

Cost Analysis

Prototype

Testing

Program Approval

Process Design

Quality Plan

Finalize Design

Vendor Selection

Tooling

Install and Debug

Full Production

Redesign # 2

This chart has been well received in the classes the author has taught. Its biggest limitation has been the general fact that almost no engineer can describe the design process in their organization (except the one who wrote it). So it seemed appropriate to develop some further examples of how QFD charts might be sequenced to correspond to the logic of design (if there is one).

The model that follows is not used in any company. It is based on a general understanding by the author of sequence of design activities in the U.S. auto industry.

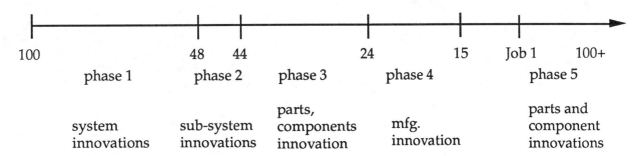

At each one of these stages QFD helps identify key innovation targets and orchestrates the systematic search for those innovations and tests proposed innovations against cost and reliability considerations. One model for innovations may be as follows:

Phase	Timing Related to Job 1	Innovation Targets
1	48 - 100 mos. before Job 1	System innovations
2	48 - 44 mos. before Job 1	Sub-System innovations
3	44 - 24 mos. before Job 1	Parts and component innovations
4	24 - 15 mos. before Job 1	Mfg. innovations
5	6 - 100+ mos. after Job 1	Parts and component innovations

These numbers are not cast in concrete, but are offered as a model. What is most important is to think of QFD as a method for prioritizing and orchestrating economic innovation at each stage of the design process.

What follows is some detail on that model. Hopefully it will help you in your process of thinking through which QFD charts are most helpful for your stage of the development process.

Appendix B

The Process of Design

The following gives a detailed, step-by-step picture for each design stage.

QFD and the Segments of New Product Development

Timeline	Segment	Name	Responsible Dep'ts.	Purpose of QFD
72 mos.	Segment 1	Advanced Eng.		Identify 2 or 3 most important system breakthroughs
48 mos.	Segment 2	Project Definition		Identify 2 or 3 most important sub-system breakthroughs
44 mos.	Segment 3	Detailed Design		Identify 2 or 3 most important part or component breakthroughs
18 mos.	Segment 4	Prototype test		Finalize manufacturing controls for critical components, parts, sub-systems, and systems

——————————————— Job #1 ———————————————

Timeline	Segment	Name	Responsible Dep'ts.	Purpose of QFD
6 -100+ mos.	Segment 5	Annual Redesign Continuous Improvement		Identify target annual breakthroughs for sub-systems, parts, components

The Process of QFD
Phase 1 - Innovation Targets

To set innovation targets, QFD uses the house of quality and design of experiments. It records these targets on several charts.

A-1 Innovation

Substitute quality characteristics (how)

A-1 Pencil	length	time between sharpening	lead dust generated	hexagonality		rate of importance	company now	competitor x	competitor y	plan	rate of improvement	sales point	absolute wt.	demanded wt
							A	2	plan	X	B	C	D	
Easy to hold	O 42			O 42		3	4	3	3	4	1		3	14
Does not smear		O 69	◎ 207			4	5	4	5	5	1	O	4.8	23
Point lasts	△ 44	◎ 396	O 132			5	4	5	3	5	1.25	◎	9.4	44
Does not roll	△ 19			◎ 171		3	3	3	3	4	1.33		4	19
Total	105	465	339	213	1122							Total	21.2	100
%	9	41	30	19	99									
company now	5"	3pgs	3g	70%										
competitor x	5"	5pgs	4g	80%										
competitor y	4"	2.5	3g	60%										
plan	5.5"	6pgs	2g	80%										

Customer Demands (what)

Main Correlations

◎ 9 = strong correlation

O 3 = some correlation

△ 1 = possible correlation

Sales points ◎= 1.5   O =1.2

$D = A \times B \times C$

$B = \dfrac{X}{2}$

B-2 Costs

Example

Chart B-2 Pencil Example	Company	Competitor x	Competitor y	Plan
Market price	15¢	18¢	14¢	16¢
Sales volume	4M	3M	8M	5M
Market share	16%	12%	32%	20%
Profit [1]	2¢	3¢	2¢	4¢
Cost [1]	13¢	15¢	12¢	12¢
				Target

Other charts include A2, A3, A4, B1, B3, B4, C2, C3, C4, and D charts.

Phase 2 - Generate Innovation Ideas

Innovation ideas are developed and recorded on:

C-1 New Technology

**First Level of Detail
Mechanisms**

new technology		writing mechanism	erasing mechanism	lead holding mechanism	chewing mechanism
	molded plastics	◯	◯		
	polymer technology	◉	◉		△
	plastic erasers		◉		
	new assembly methods	△			

E-1 New Concepts

New Concepts

		spring loaded lead	retractable lead	Datum best in class	friction fit eraser	pocket clip	china pencil
Chart E-1 Pencil example							
Customer Demands	easy to hold			Quill		−	
	does not smear		+	E. F.			−
	point lasts	+	+				−
	does not roll					+	−
	Cost	−	−		+	−	+
	+'s	1+	2+		1+	1+	
	−'s	1−	1−			1−	3−

Other charts include E-2, E-3, E-4, and F-1.

Phase 3 - Innovation Engineering

F1 Value Engineering

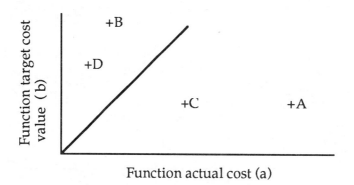

Function actual cost (a)

F2 Revised

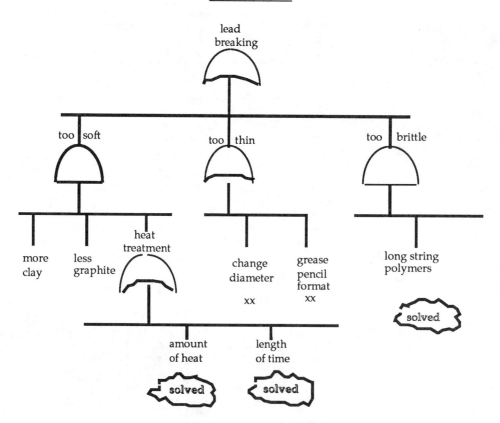

Other charts include F3.

Phase 4 - Manufacturing Controls
Some charts help develop manufacturing controls.

G3

Chart G3 Process Planning Chart

No.	Process	Conditions of Manufacturing		Parts Characteristics	Control points of Process
		Equipment	Index		
1	obtain steel			freedom from rust	incoming observation
2	form wire	extruder		diameter flex	O.D. Dimension degree of flex
3	coil wire	coiler		tension	amount of spring level of recoil
4	cut spring	crimp		smooth	degree of smoothness

G6

Q.C. Process Chart

Dept Name/# QHD/ 101	section head Y. Akao
date prepared 7/15/87	preparer Bob King
revisions 12/19/87	

Part Name/Number	Flow chart		process name	work instruction sheet #	process control item	Control Method							Inspection item	Inspection method					
	raw material	process				person in charge	place	when	measurement	sampling method	standard	control data		person in charge	sensory data	instruction sheet #	sampling method	record kept	in charge of action
spring			obtain steel																
			store steel	102	lot #'s	a	ware-house K	1 mo.	count	100%	zero defects	check sheet	rust	c	see	—		log sheet	e
			form wire																
			coil wire	104	temperature	e	coiler 6	every 30 min	temp. guage	once 30 min.	F degrees	control chart	spring tension	d	feel	tension testor	5 every 20 min.	control chart	f
			cut spring																
			inspection																

Other charts include G1, G2, G4, and G5.

Summary Sheet of Charts Used in Each QFD Segment

Segment 1 = o
Segment 2 = x
o = used before
x = new use
o/x = revised

Segment 1
11 new

12 new

3 repeat

	A	B	C systems	D Rel	E NC	F
1	o	o	o	x	o/x	o/x
2	o	o	o	x	o/x	o/x
3	x	o	o	x	o/x	o/x
sub-systems 4	x	x	x	x	o/x	o/x

Segment 3

7 new
17 repeat

	A	B	C sub-systems	D	E	F
1	o	o	o/x	o/x	o/x	o/x
2	o	o	o/x	o/x	o/x	o/x
3	o	o	o/x	o/x	o/x	o/x
parts, components, raw materials 4	o/x	o/x	o/x	o/x	o/x	o/x

	1	2	3	4	5	6
G	o	o	o	o	o	o

Segment 4

6+ repeat

	1	2	3	4	5	6
G	o/x	o/x	o/x	o/x	o/x	o/x

Segment 5

Varies with situation.

Design Stage 1 - Advanced Engineering
Phase 1 - Innovation Targets for Systems

Task/Chart	Purpose/Comments
I-1 Matrix Data Analysis	Decide what business you are in

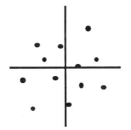

| **I-2**
New Concept
Selection Chart | "Blue Sky"
New directions for product |

| **I-3**
Market Research
Kano 3 Arrows
and Survey
Results Matrix | Determine "voice of customer" |

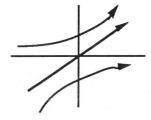

| **I-4**
K-J and Tree
2 levels | Understand voice"
of customer" |

     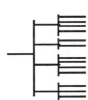

I - 5
A-1 Part 1
House of Quality

Learn customer
priorities

I - 6
A-1 Quality
Characteristics

Purpose
• Identify key items to
measure and control
• Bench-marking/
Competitive analysis
• Preliminary targets

I - 7
A-2 Voice of
Engineer (Function)
vs. Quality
Characteristics
B-1 Part 1
Voice of Eng.
vs. Voice of
Customer

• Identify missing quality
characteristics
• Identify over-design
• Learn engineering
priorities (Saaty method)
• Learn conflicts between
voice of engineer and
voice of customer
• Alternate approach to
learn engineering
priorities

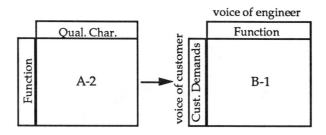

I - 8
B-3 Factor Analysis
(Taguchi)
Breakthrough targets

In light of combined
voice of customer and
voice of engineer
• Analyze needed break-
throughs (factor analysis)
• Set preliminary
breakthrough targets

Phase 2 - Innovation Ideas for Systems

I - 9
C-1 New Technology
vs. Systems

In light of breakthrough
targets
• Identify potential new
technology
• Select system changes
based on new technology

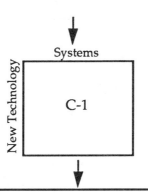

I - 10
C-2 Part 1
Systems vs.
Functions

Identify key systems based
on voice of engineer
(functions)

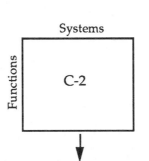

I -11
C-3 Part 1
Systems vs.
Quality
Characteristics

Identify key systems based
on quality characteristics

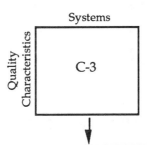

I -12
B-2 Cost Analysis
Total Vehicle
(Preliminary)

In light of key systems
and potential new
technology do prelim-
inary cost targets

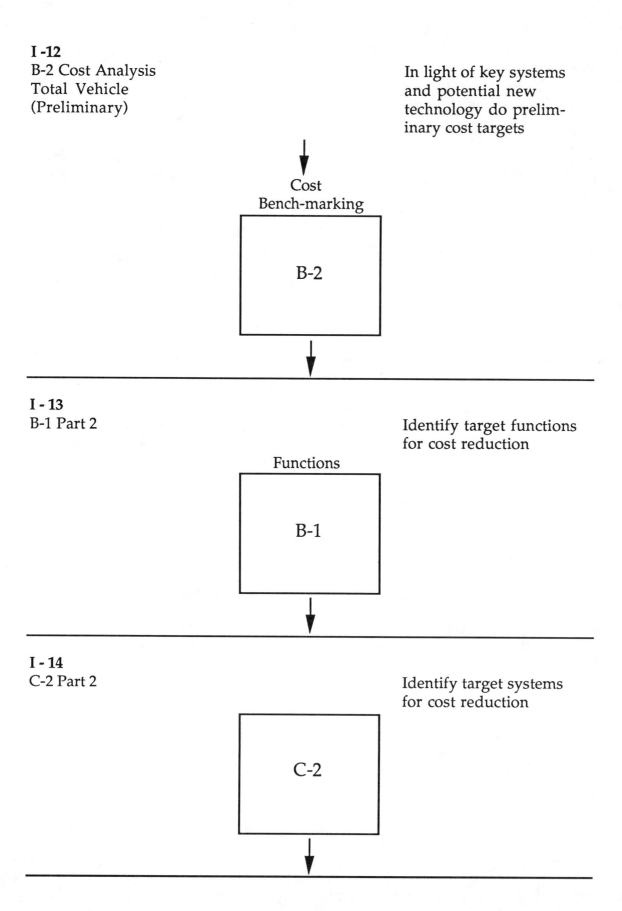

Cost
Bench-marking

B-2

I - 13
B-1 Part 2

Identify target functions
for cost reduction

Functions

B-1

I - 14
C-2 Part 2

Identify target systems
for cost reduction

C-2

Phase 3 - Innovation Engineering for Systems

I - 15
F-3 Reviewed
Dendogram

Draw a diagram of potential system and cost improvements based on learnings of I - 8 through I - 14 and record on reviewed dendogram

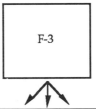

I - 16
F-1, F-2, F-3
Value Eng.
Factor Analysis
Finite Element
Method

• Develop engineering breakthroughs on systems and cost using value engineering, factor analysis, finite element method, and other tools of engineering breakthrough

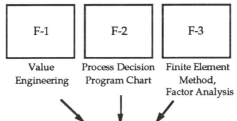

I - 17
Revise cost
analysis B-2
based on eng.
breakthroughs

• Evaluate competitive cost position based on eng. breakthroughs
• If satisfactory go on to step I - 18
• If not satisfactory review steps I - 13, I -14, I - 15, and I - 16 for alternatives

---

I - 18
Revise targets
A-1 based on
eng. and cost
breakthroughs

• Check to see how new
systems and new technol-
ogy stack up against
competitors

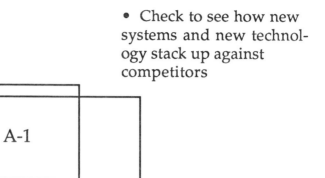

I - 19
Cost/Benefit Analysis

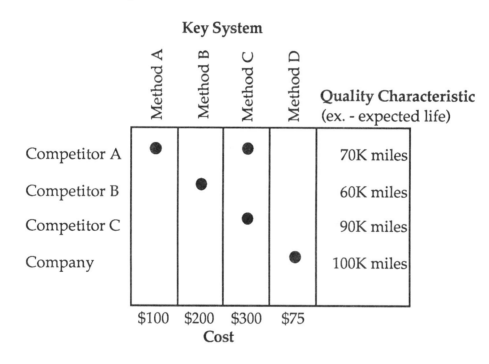

Segment 2
QFD and New Product Development

Segment II Project Definition (48 mos. before Job 1)
Phase 1 - Innovation Targets for Sub-Systems

II - 1
Review charts
from segment I

A-1 Key customer demands, key quality
      characteristics

A-2 Voice of the engineer, key quality
      characteristics

B-1 Voice of the customer vs. voice of
      the engineer

B-2 Cost targets for product

B-3 Preliminary breakthrough targets

C-1 System changes suggested by new
      technology

C-2 System changes suggested by voice
      engineer

C-3 System changes suggested by quality
      characteristics

F-1 Cost reductions of functions and systems
      as prioritized by B-1 and C-2

F-2 System changes based on Process-
      Decision-Program Chart and Finite
      Element Method

F-3 System changes based on factor analysis
      and reviewed dendogram

II - 2
A-4
Sub-System Chart

<u>Purpose</u>
• Identify the key sub-systems for improvement based on the ones that have strong relationship with key (top 2 or 3) quality characteristics

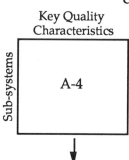

II - 3
B-4
Key sub-systems and
key quality characteristics

<u>Purpose/Comments</u>
• Identify the key functions and key quality characteristics for each of the key (2-3) sub-systems and capability indices

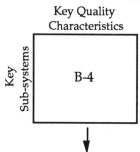

Phase 2 - Innovation Ideas for Sub-Systems

II - 4
C-4
Sub-systems
vs. systems

• Identify sub-systems that relate to key systems
• Identify targets for sub-system cost reduction

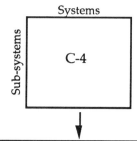

II - 5
D-1
Fault tree
analysis vs.
customer demands

• Prioritize reliability problems
to work on based on customer
demands

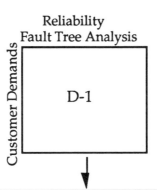

II - 6
D-2
Fault tree
analysis vs.
functions

• Prioritize reliability problems
to work on based on voice of
engineer (functions)

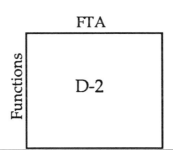

II - 7
D-3
Fault tree
analysis vs.
quality characteristics

• Prioritize reliability problems
to work on based on critical
quality characteristics

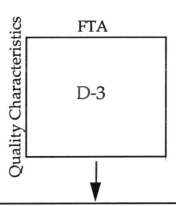

II - 8
D-4
Sub-system failure
modes vs. parts

• Prioritize the development of
sub-system product FMEA's
based on an analysis of sub-
system failure modes

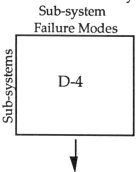

II - 9
E-1
New concepts for
sub-systems vs.
customer demands

• Pre-select new sub-system
concepts based on meeting
voice of customer

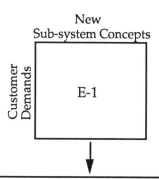

II - 10
E-2
New concepts for
sub-systems vs.
voice of the engin-
eer (functions)

• Pre-select new sub-system
concepts based on meeting
voice of the engineer

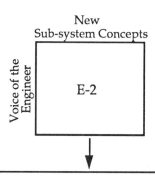

II - 11
E-3
New concepts for sub-systems
vs. critical quality characteristics.

• Pre-select new sub-system
concepts based on meeting
critical quality characteristics

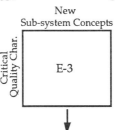

II - 12
E-4
New concepts for
sub-systems
summary

• Identify strengths and
weaknesses of new concepts
based on whether they are
better or worse than existing
product or best in class product
when compared to customer
demands, functions, and critical
quality characteristics

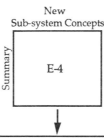

Phase 3 - Innovation Engineering for Sub-Systems

II - 13
F-3
Reviewed
Dendogram

• Draw a diagram of potential
sub-system and cost improvements based on learnings of
steps II - 2 through step II - 12

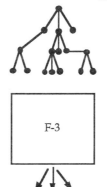

II - 14
F-1, F-2, F-3

• Develop engineering breakthroughs on systems and cost using value engineering, factor analysis, finite element method, Process-Decision-Program Chart, and other engineering breakthrough tools

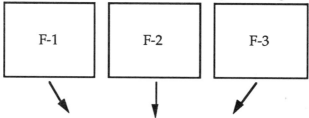

II - 15
B-2
Revise cost analysis based on engineering breakthroughs

• Evaluate competitive cost position based on engineering breakthroughs. If satisfactory go on to II - 16. If not, review steps 13 and 14.

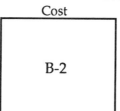

II - 16
A-4
Critical quality characteristics vs. new sub-systems

• Redo Chart A-4 based on new sub-systems developed in steps II - 9 through II - 14

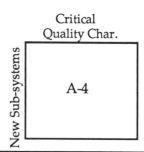

II - 17
B-4
Quality characteristics,
functions, and Cp
vs. key sub-systems

• Analyze key new sub-systems
for function and quality
characteristics

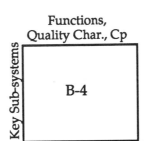

Functions,
Quality Char., Cp

Key Sub-systems

B-4

QFD and New Product Development
Segment 3
Detailed Design (44 -38 mos. before Job 1)
Phase 1 - Innovation Targets for Parts and Components

III - 1
Review charts from Segment II

A-1 Charts Voice of customer, key quality characteristics, key system changes
and approaches, competitive analyses

A-2 Chart voice of engineer, key quality characteristics

A-3 Sub-system trade offs/conflicts

A-4 Key old sub-systems, key new sub-systems

B-1 Conflicts between voice of customer and voice of engineer

B-2 Cost targets - competitive analysis

B-3 Breakthrough targets for key quality characteristics

B-4 Sub-system quality characteristics, old and new cp targets, etc.

C-1, 2, 3, 4 System priority selection reasons

B-1, C-2, C-4 Cost reduction targets for functions, systems and sub-systems

D-1, 2, 3, 4 Reliability priorities for sub-systems based on customers, engineers, and quality characteristics

E-1, 2, 3, 4 New sub-system concept priorities based on voice of customers, engineers, and critical quality characteristics

F-1, 2, 3 Sub-system changes developed through value-engineering, factor analysis, finite element method, etc.

III - 2
A-4
Parts, components, and
raw materials vs. key
quality characteristics

• Identify key parts, components, and raw materials to be
improved based on strong
relationship to key quality
characteristics

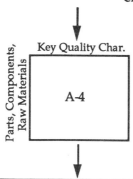

III - 3
B-4
Key parts, components,
and raw materials vs.
quality characteristics

• Identify the key functions,
key quality characteristics, and
capability indices for each of the
key (2 - 3) parts, components,
and raw materials

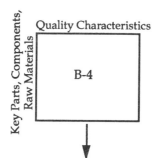

Phase 2 - Innovation Ideas for Parts and Components

III -4
C-1
New technology vs.
sub-systems

• Identify potential sub-system changes based on new technology

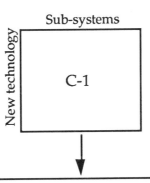

III - 5
C-2
Sub-systems vs.
voice of engineer
functions

• Identify potential sub-system changes based on voice of the engineer (functions)

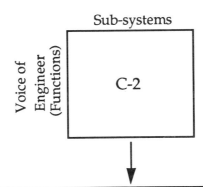

III - 6
C-3
Sub-systems vs. key
quality characteristics

• Identify potential sub-system changes based on key quality characteristics

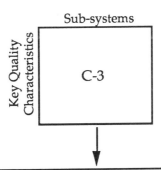

III - 7

C-4

Sub-system vs. parts,
components, and
raw materials

• Identify priority parts, components, and raw materials for
cost reduction

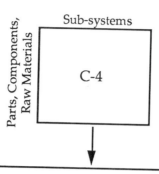

III- 8

D-4

Parts, components, and
raw material failure modes
vs. parts, components, and
raw materials

• Prioritize development of
parts, components, and raw
material product FMEA's
based on strong relationships
with failure modes of same

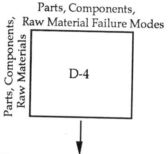

III - 9

E-1

New concepts for parts,
components, vs.
customer demands

• Pre-select new concepts for
parts and components based
on meeting voice of the
customer

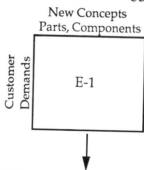

III - 10
E-2
New concepts for parts
and components vs.
voice of engineer

• Pre-select new concepts for
parts and components based on
meeting voice of the engineer

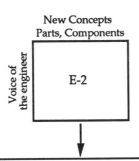

III - 11
E-3
New concepts for parts
and components vs.
key quality characteristics

• Pre-select new concepts for
parts and components based on
meeting key quality
characteristics

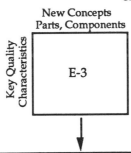

III - 12
E-4
New concepts for parts
and components summary

• Identify strengths and weaknesses of new concepts for parts
and components based on
whether they are better or worse
than existing product or best in
class product when compared to
customer demands, functions,
and critical quality
characteristics

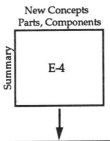

Phase 3 - Innovation Engineering for Parts and Components

III - 13
F-3
Reviewed Dendogram

• Draw a diagram of potential part, component, and raw material improvements based on learnings of steps II - 2 through II - 12

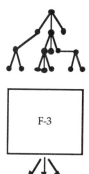

III - 14
F-1, F-2, F-3

• Develop engineering break-throughs on sub-systems, parts, and components using VE, PDPC, FEM, factor analysis, etc.

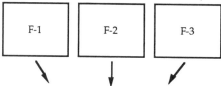

Task/Chart
III - 15
F-4
Summary of engineering breakthroughs

Purpose/Comments
• Summarize engineering breakthroughs regarding sub-systems, parts, components, and raw materials, cost savings vs. target, and items critical for function, reliability and assembly

Summary of engineering breakthroughs, parts, etc.

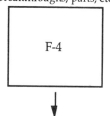

III - 16
B-2
Review cost analysis
based on engineering
breakthroughs

• Evaluate competitive cost
position based on engineering
breakthroughs
• If acceptable, go on to III - 17.
If not, review III - 9 through
III - 14

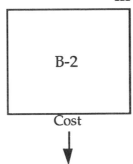

Cost

III - 17
A-4
Critical quality characteristics
vs. new parts, components,
and raw materials

• Re-do Chart A-4 based on
new parts, components, and
raw materials developed in
steps III - 8 through III - 14

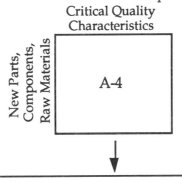

III - 18
B-4
Functions, quality characteristics
and Cp vs. key new parts,
components, and raw materials

• Analyze key new parts,
components, and raw materials
for function, quality characteristics, and Cp

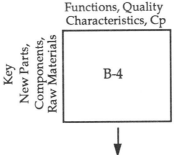

Phase 4 - Manufacturing Controls for Parts and Components

III - 19
G-1
QA Table

• Identify key quality designs, quality characteristics, and reasons for key parts and components

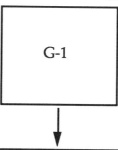

III - 20
G-2
Purchasing Chart

• Select best supplier based on quality and cost and other appropriate measures

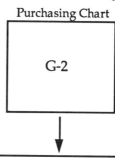

III - 21
G-3
Process Planning Chart

• Identify the parts, characteristics, conditions of manufacturing (equipment and settings and control points of the process)

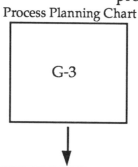

III - 22
G-4
Process Fault
Tree Analysis

• Identify potential process
failure modes.

Process Fault
Tree Analysis

```
┌─────────────────┐
│                 │
│                 │
│       G-4       │
│                 │
│                 │
└─────────────────┘
         │
         ▼
```

III - 23
G-5
Process Failure Mode
and Effect Analysis

• Identify the level of occur-
ance, severity, and detection of
failure modes

Process FMEA

```
┌─────────────────┐
│                 │
│                 │
│       G-5       │
│                 │
│                 │
└─────────────────┘
```

III - 24
G-6
QC Process Chart

• Identify the plan for process
controls and inspection controls

QC Process Chart

```
┌─────────────────┐
│                 │
│                 │
│       G-6       │
│                 │
│                 │
└─────────────────┘
```

QFD and New Product Development
Segment 4
Prototype/Test
Revise Manufacturing Controls

Task/Chart   **Purpose/Comments**
IV - 1

Review A, B, C, D, E, F Charts from Phase III and make technical changes
based on prototypes and tests. Save breakthroughs and inventions for next
model unless savings is considerable, in which case seek appropriate waivers.

IV - 2
G-1
QA Table

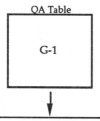

• Update QA table based on learnings from prototype/tests

IV - 3
G-2
Purchasing Chart

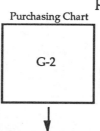

• Update purchasing charts based on learnings from prototype/tests

IV - 4
G-3
Process Planning Chart

• Update process planning chart based on learnings from prototype/tests

IV - 5
G-4
Process Fault
Tree Analysis

• Update process fault tree
analysis based on learnings
from prototype/tests

Process FTA

```
┌─────────────────┐
│                 │
│      G-4        │
│                 │
└─────────────────┘
         │
         ▼
```

IV - 6
G-5
Process Failure Mode
and Effect Analysis

• Update process FMEA based
on learnings from prototype/
tests

Process FMEA

```
┌─────────────────┐
│                 │
│      G-5        │
│                 │
└─────────────────┘
```

IV - 7
G-6
QC Process Chart

• Update QC process chart based
on learnings from prototype/
tests

QC Process Chart

```
┌─────────────────┐
│                 │
│      G-6        │
│                 │
└─────────────────┘
```

Appendix C Glossary

<u>Priority</u>: QFD is a pareto chart. In each case we are looking to identify the key systems, sub-systems, parts and manufacturing controls that will lead to significant improvements in market share. In some cases breakthroughs come from new technology, in other cases from new concepts.

<u>Affordable</u>: QFD is pareto chart dedicated to cost reduction. It compares cost and real value and targets those items that have relatively high cost and low value for cost reduction. It identifies priority cost reductions for systems, sub-systems, parts, and functions.

<u>Customer-Focused</u>: QFD begins with the voice of the customer - that is the final consumer! But it also includes the voice of the engineer by focusing and functions and it assists the development of trade-offs when the voice of the customer is in conflict with the voice of the engineer.

<u>Innovation Targets</u>: Breakthrough targets based on customer priorities, comparative analysis of competitors and marketing potential.

<u>Cost Targets</u>: Targets based on what marketplace will pay and desired profit.

<u>Innovation Possibilities</u>: Initial estimates of possible breakthroughs.

<u>Innovation Engineering</u>: Work on innovations to see if they can be accomplished.

Appendix D
Guidelines for Facilitators

Customer Demand Rules

1. Clear to everyone in the producer organization

2. Positive statement ideally

3. No numbers (customers buy benefits, not features)

4. Use definition (so everyone will understand)

5. Trail to customer information

Note: Government and other problems - -
- you can't talk to customer
- you can only talk to the engineer,
who doesn't know what the customer wants

Rules for Forming Practice Groups

1. Groups should be 1 - 4. Purpose is to practice tools and not group dynamics
        Organize by company or product group

2. Pick a product that is already designed
        If not, there will be too much new
        New method, new product
        Pick product you are familiar with

3. Think about one customer for product. We will look later at how to
        handle multiple customers.

4. On KJ do 10 - 15 items
        Do tree - add several more
        Pick 6 or 8 items at second or third level to use on the matrix chart
        (In reality you may have 50 - 300 items depending on the complexity of
        the product)

Instructions for Filling Out Ratings on Customer Demands

1. Fill out items across, pick one item, do rate of importance, company now,
    competition, plan, etc.

2. Rate of importance - There should be a range of distribution from at least 3
    - 5. Because of selecting just key items, you may want to have all 5's.
    In this case think of decimal points.

3. Plan is a real key item - Think of what decision rules you will use (e.g., cost,
    competition, engineering feasibility, return on investment).

Rules for Substitute Quality Characteristics

(Substitute Quality Characteristics are the How)

1. Should be measurable or controllable
        If I control/measure --------I will meet this customer demand

2. No names of parts (these will be considered in another chart)

3. No tests (put instead what the test measures)

4. No process names (this will be covered in another chart)

5. List at least one or more substitute quality characteristics for each customer
        demand

Instructions for Practicing Substitute Quality Characteristics

1. Pick 8 - 10 second or third level customer demands

2. List for each customer demand one or more substitute characteristics

3. Normally at this point you would do an Affinity (KJ) Chart to find the appropriate categories. Then do a Tree Diagram (System Chart) to detail substitute quality characteristics listing with detailed items answering the question "how accomplished" for more general items

4. Pick 8 - 10 second or third level substitute quality characteristics for practice

Benefits of QFD

1. Strategic choices for <u>increased market share</u>.

2. <u>Better communication</u> between departments.

3. <u>Focused effort</u>. Product or service priorities known by all.

4. <u>Reduced engineering changes</u> on critical design elements.

5. <u>Better controls</u> of critical elements of critical designs.

6. <u>Better reliability</u> of critical design elements.

7. Openness to <u>new concepts</u>.

8. <u>Cost reduction</u> (value engineering integrated with QFD).

9. Competitive <u>bench marking</u>.

10. <u>Cross training</u> of design engineers.

11. Integration of several improvement tools (e.g., factor analysis, VE, SPC, and documentation).
    - Justification for use of tools
    - Targeting the use of tools
    - Leveraged use of D.O.E.

12. Better understanding of customer demands.

13. Better understanding of different customers.

14. Better understanding of conflicting customer demands.

15. Better understanding of engineering requirements.

16. Better understanding of conflicting engineering requirements.

17. Improved structuring of the design process.

18. Better understanding of quality in general.
    - practical nature of quality
    - by new groups design, marketing

19. Better market research.

- More focused to real design issues
- Focus groups by design engineers
- Direct contact between customer and designer and mfg.

20. Establishes a critical path.
    Traceability from final product to customer demand.

21. Build in quality upstream.

22. Improved documentation.

23. Common language for all departments.

24. Identifying customer(s)
    - Different customer groups
    - Defining customer groups

25. Break down walls.

26. Makes quality real - touch, taste, feel.

27. Improve internal budgeting (potentially).

28. Better planning - individual efforts fit into product.

29. How individual efforts fit into product.

30. Why designs are set the way they are.

31. Potentially early identification of conflicting Quality Characteristics - downstream fixing consumer problems without causing other problems.

Opposition to QFD

1. People who participate in Mega Charts. 10,000 + correlations

2. Payoff not clear. Learning Curve

3. QFD - long term rather than short term.

4. I don't understand it.

5. I already have 130% job.

6. Not another program?

7. It is new.

8. No integration of TQC elements.

9. Opposition to management by committee.

10. Other ways to improve communication.

11. A new fad!

12. System not fully understood and documented.

13. Training still in transition.

14. Limited resources.

15. More complicated case study.

16. Tried for 2 hrs. and it didn't work.

17. Translation to non-mfg.

18. Stifles innovation - too organized - design is an art form.

19. Lack of documented success.

20. Difficulty of viewing actual case studies.

21. Made in Japan - cultural issues.

22. Americans not detail oriented.

23. QFD is hard to view in a stand alone environment.

24. QFD tried without TQC is less successful.

25.
Sell A -1 alone

Strengths	Weaknesses
• Good method for bench marking	•Difficult to come to specific components, etc.
• Method for integrating • Customer input by a common language	• Never really leverage to mfg./downstream.
•Gives sense of realism to understanding customer.	• Marketing not understanding mfg. and vice versa.
• A-1 chart has the highest leverage.	• Problem solving vs. process improvement.
	• Risk of incomplete A-1.
	• Mixed items in A-1.
	• Could be the wrong tool.

U.S. QFD Successes to Date

1. Clarification of engineering requirements Ford Lt. Truck.

2. Improved sales P & G Hotel products.

3. Improved internal customer/supplier relationship - Digital.

4. Improved external customer/supplier relationship - Ford, Climate Control, Cirtek, GE, and others.

5. Improved manufacturing documentation and control - G.E. Motor.

6. Improved software design - H.P. and Digital.

7. Improved education of new engineers - Cirtek.

8. Prioritization and scheduling of design effort - Cirtek.

9. Improved new product design and launch - Masland.

10. New design system - Kendal.

11. Clarification and prioritization of customer demands - Digital.

12. Customer driven quality characteristics, and quality in daily work - FPL.

13. Better documentation of customer demands - all.

Most Frequent QFD Errors

1. Charts too big. Chart A-1 is a pareto chart - not improved by more items.

2. Only use A-1.
   - Knowing in written detail what the customer wants is important.
   - Doing something about it is probably more important.
   - Putting everything (e.g., cost, reliability, wants, functions in the chart is often confusing and misleading.

3. QFD if mandated. QFD, if done properly, is complex. As a ritual it will not be understood.

4. Parts should not be mixed with substitute quality characteristics.
   - Parts belong in A-4
   - Parts are different from quality characteristics

5. Engineering demands should not be mixed with consumer demands.
   - Consumer demands should be in chart A-1.
   - Engineering demands should be in chart A-2.

6. Consumers should not be asked about things they know nothing about.

7. Do QFD when it is too late to make changes or there is no buy-in for changes.

QFD Prerequisites

1. The better understanding and use of TQC, the better.

2. Some team expertise in market research, focus groups, UE, factor analysis, SPC, reliability tools, Pugh, etc. is helpful.

3. A facilitator or leader who thoroughly understands QFD.

4. Steering Committee: Collecting and disseminating information/charts. Quality of information.

Size of Teams

1. 1 - 15   5 or 6 with delegated work is better.

Problems Overcome

1. People who won't participate - do work and send it out for comments - they may be willing to criticize.

How to Select and Facilitate QFD Projects
Select:

1. Identify projects that support company priorities.

2. Select projects that will improve key interfaces.

3. Involve all essential departments to accomplish goals.

4. Involve personnel who believe QFD will work.

5. Select projects that are likely to succeed.

6. Select projects that are likely to generate significant success.

Facilitate

1. Clearly define project.

2. Obtain management commitment to take action on findings.

3. Focus on process rather than content of project. (Facilitator)

Top Management's Job Regarding QFD

1. Make training available.

2. Set clear priorities for QFD activities.

3. Make it clear that QFD is a priority.

4. Insist that product design decisions be based on facts.

5. Assure that QFD leaders thoroughly understand the benefits, pitfalls, and proper procedures for QFD.

6. Do not make QFD mandatory.

7. Understand the details and requirements of successful QFD.

8. More than one leader.

Appendix E
The Seven Management Tools

General Planning

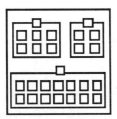

The **Affinity Diagram (KJ)** gathers large amounts of data and organizes it into groupings based on the natural relationship between each item.

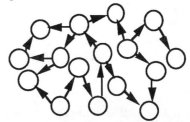

The **Interrelationship Diagraph** explores and displays interrelated factors involved in complex problems. It shows the relationships between factors.

Intermediate Planning

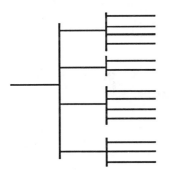

The **Tree Diagram** systematically maps out the full range of tasks/methods needed to achieve a goal.

The **Matrix Diagram** displays the relationship between necessary tasks and people or other tasks, often to show responsibility for tasks.

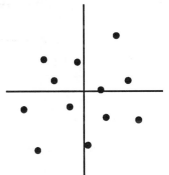

Matrix Data Analysis shows the strength of the relationship between variables which have been statistically determined.

Detailed Planning

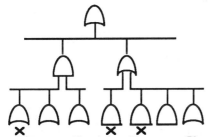

The **PDPC (Process Decision Program Chart)** maps out every conceivable event that may occur when moving from a problem statement to the possible solutions.

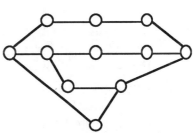

The **Arrow Diagram** is used to plan the most appropriate schedule for any task and to control it effectively during its progress.

Affinity Diagram/KJ Method

Definition

This tool gathers large amounts of language data (ideas, opinions, issues, etc.) and organizes them into groupings based on the natural relationship between each item. It is largely a creative rather than a logical process.

The biggest obstacle to planning for improvement is past success or failure. It is assumed that what worked or failed in the past will continue to do so in the future. We therefore perpetuate patterns of thinking that may or may not be appropriate. Continuous improvement requires that new logical patterns be explored at all times.

The KJ Method is an excellent way to get a group of people to react from the creative "gut level" rather than from the intellectual, logical level. It also efficiently organizes these creative new thought patterns for further elaboration. Teams may produce and organize more than 100 ideas or issues in 30-45 minutes. Think of how long that task would take using a traditional discussion process. It is not only efficient, however. It also encourages *true* participation because every person's ideas find their way into the process. This differs from many discussions in which ideas are lost in the shuffle and are therefore never considered.

When to Use the Affinity Diagram/KJ Method

We have yet to find an issue for which KJ has not proven helpful. However, there are applications that are more natural than others. The "cleanest" use of KJ is in situations in which:

a.   **Facts or thoughts are in chaos.** When issues seem too large or complex to grasp, try KJ to "map the geography" of the issue.

b.   **Breakthrough in traditional concepts is needed.** When the only solutions are old solutions, try KJ to expand the team's thinking.

c.   **Support for a solution is essential for successful implementation.**

KJ is **not** suggested for use when a problem: 1) is simple, or 2) requires a very quick solution.

Construction of an Affinity Diagram/KJ Method

The most effective group to assemble to do a KJ is one that has the knowledge needed to uncover the various dimensions of the issue. It also seems to work most smoothly when the team is accustomed to working together. This enables team members to speak in a type of shorthand because of their common experiences. There should be a maximum of six to eight members on the team.

The following are the most commonly used construction steps:

1. Phrase the issue to be considered. It works best when vaguely stated. For example, "What are the issues surrounding top management's support for a CWQC process?" There should be no more explanation than that since more details may prejudice the responses in the "old direction".

2. The responses can be recorded in one of two ways:

    a. Recorded on a flip chart pad and then transcribed onto small cards (e.g., 1" X 3"), one idea per card.

    b. Recorded directly onto individual cards by a recorder or by the contributor him- or herself. **Note:** It must be stressed that ideas should be concise and recorded exactly as stated. The aim should be to capture the essence of the thought.

3. The team should take the cards, mix them, and spread them out randomly on a large table.

4. The cards can be grouped by the team or assigned to an individual in the following way:

    a. Look for two cards that seem to be related in some way. Place those to one side. Look for other related cards.

    b. Repeat this process until you have all possible cards placed in no more than ten groupings. Do not force-fit single cards into groupings where they don't belong. These single cards ("loners") may form their own grouping or may never find a "home".

Note 1: Do not refer to these as "categories". They are simply groupings of ideas that hang together. There is a difference between the two words.

Note 2: It seems to be most effective to have everyone move the cards at will without talking. This forces team members not to get trapped in semantic battles.

c. Look for a card in each grouping that captures the meaning of that group. This card is placed at the top of the grouping. If there is not such a card in the grouping, then one must be written. This card should be simply and concisely written. Gather each grouping with the header card on the top.

5. Transfer the information from cards onto paper with lines around each grouping. Related clusters should be placed near each other with connecting lines. (See Figure 4.1) This is the first round of the KJ process and should be presented for additions, deletions, and modifications.

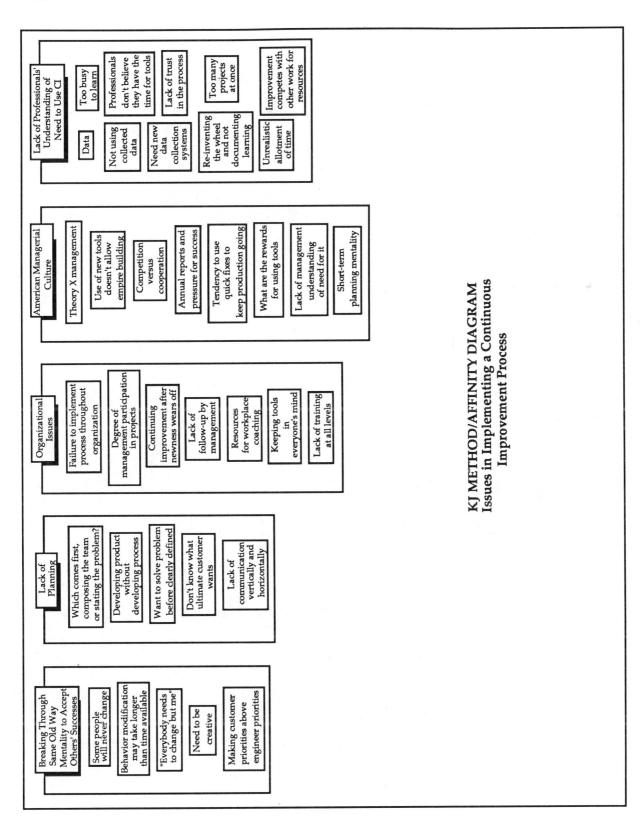

KJ METHOD/AFFINITY DIAGRAM
Issues in Implementing a Continuous
Improvement Process

FIGURE 4.1

Interrelationship Digraph

Definition

This tool takes a central idea, issue, or problem and maps out the logical or sequential links among related items. While still a very creative process, the Interrelationship Digraph begins to draw the logical connections that the KJ Method surfaces.

In planning and problem solving, it is obviously not enough to just create an explosion of ideas. The KJ Method allows some initial organized creative patterns to emerge, but the Interrelationship Digraph (ID) lets **logical** patterns become apparent. This is based on the same principle that the Japanese frequently apply regarding the natural emergence of ideas. Therefore, an ID starts from a central concept, leads to the generation of large quantities of ideas and finally the delineation of observed patterns. To some this may appear to be like reading tea leaves, but it works incredibly well. Like the KJ, the ID allows those unanticipated ideas and connections to rise to the surface.

When to Use the Interrelationship Digraph

We have found the ID to be exceptionally adaptable to both specific operational issues and general organizational questions. For example, a classic use of the ID at Toyota focused on all of the factors involved in the establishment of a "billboard system" as part of the JIT program. On the other hand, it has also been used to deal with issues underlying the problem of getting top management support for TQC.

In summary, the ID should be used when:

a) An issue is sufficiently complex that the interrelationship between ideas is difficult to determine.

b) The correct sequencing of management actions is critical.

c) There is a feeling that the problem under discussion is only a symptom.

d) There is ample time to complete the required reiterative process.

Construction of an Interrelationship Digraph

As in the KJ diagram and the remainder of the tools, the aim is to have **the right people, with the right tools working on the right problems.** This means that the first step is to define the necessary blend of people for a group of 6 - 8 individuals.

The construction steps are as follows:

1. **Clearly** make one statement that states the key issue under discussion.
    Note: The source of this issue can vary. It may come from a problem that presents itself clearly. In this case, the ID would be the first step in the cycle rather than the KJ. The KJ is frequently used to generate the key issues to be explored in the ID.

2. Record the issue/problem statement. It can be recorded by:
    a)   Placing it on the same type of card as is used in the KJ.
    b)   Writing it on a flip chart.

3. To start the process, place the statement in one of two patterns:
    a)   A centralized pattern in which the statement is placed in the middle of the table or flip chart paper with related ideas clustered around it.
    b)   A unidirectional pattern in which the statement is placed to the extreme right or left of the table or flip chart paper with related ideas posted on one side of it.

4. Generate the related issues/problems in the following ways:
    a)   Take the cards from a grouping under KJ and lay them out with the one that is most closely related to the problem statement placed next to it. Then lay out the rest of the cards in sequential or causal order.

    b)   Do wide-open brainstorming, place the ideas on cards and cluster them around the Central Statement as in "a".

    c)   Do wide-open brainstorming but directly onto the flip chart instead of cards. Proceed as in "a" or "b".

Note 1: The advantage of using cards is that they can be moved as the discussion progresses. The flip chart method is quicker but can become very messy if changes occur.

Note 2: When using the flip chart method, designate all the related ideas by placing them in a single lined box.

5. Once all of the related idea statements are placed relative to the central problem statement, fill in the causal arrows that indicate what leads to what. Look for possible relationships between each issue and every other issue.
    Note: At this step you would look for patterns of arrows to determine what the key factors/causes are. For example, if one factor had seven arrows coming from it to other issues, while all others had three or less, then that would be a key factor. It would be designated by a double hatched box.

6. Copy the ID legibly and circulate identified key factors to group members.

7. As in the KJ, you may draw lines around groupings of related issues.

8. Prepare to use the identified key factors as the basis for the next tool, **The Tree Diagram.**

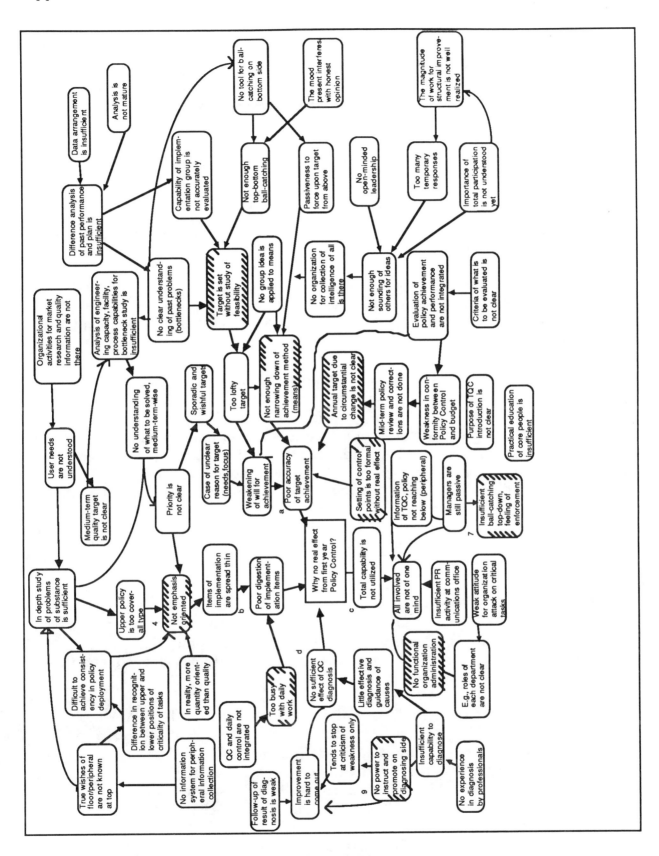

FIGURE 4.2

SYSTEM FLOW/TREE DIAGRAM

Definition

This tool systematically maps out the full range of paths and tasks that needs to be accomplished in order to achieve a primary goal and every related sub-goal. In the original Japanese context, it describes the "methods" by which every "purpose" is to be achieved.

In many ways, the KJ Method and Interrelationship Digraph force the key issues to the surface. The questions then become, "What is the sequence of tasks that need to be completed in order to best address that issue?" or "What are all of the factors which contribute to the existence of the key problem?" The Tree Diagram is appropriate for either question. Therefore, it can either be used as a cause-finding problem solver or a task-generating planning tool. In either use it brings the process from a broad level of concern to the lowest practical level of detail.

Another strong point is that it forces the user to examine the logical link between all of the interim tasks. This addresses the tendency of many managers to jump from the broad goal to details without examining what needs to happen in order for successful implementation to occur. It also rapidly uncovers gaps in logic or planning.

When to Use the Tree Diagram

The Tree Diagram is indispensable when you require a thorough understanding of what needs to be accomplished, how it is to be achieved, and the relationships between these goals and methodologies.

It has been found to be most helpful in situations such as the following:

a.   **When you need to translate ill-defined needs into operational characteristics.** For example, a Tree Diagram would be helpful in converting a desire to have an "easy to use VCR" into every product characteristic that would contribute to this goal. It would also identify which characteristics can presently be controlled.

b.   **When you need to explore all the possible causes of a problem.**
      This use is closest to the Cause & Effect Diagram (Fishbone Chart). For example, it could be used to uncover all of the reasons why top management may not support a continuous improvement effort.

c.   **When you need to identify the first task that must be accomplished when aiming for a broad organizational goal.** For example, the Tree Diagram would be very helpful to the coordinator of Quality Improvement Programs who wants to know what is already being accomplished and where the key gaps exist.

d.   **When the issue under question has sufficient complexity and time available for solution.** For example, a Tree Diagram would not be particularly helpful for deciding how to deal with a product contamination problem that is shutting down your production line. It could be used to prevent it from reoccurring, but not in deciding on the stop-gap measures to be taken.

NOTE: In its most common usage the Tree Diagram conceptually resembles the Cause & Effect Diagrams. We have found it to be easier to interpret because of its clear, linear layout. It also seems to create fewer "loose ends" than the C&E.

Construction of a System Flow/Tree Diagram

It has been shown that these tools are most powerful when used in combination, but they are also very effective when applied singly. With this in mind the following are the most widely used steps:

1.   Agree upon one statement that clearly and simply states the core issue, problem, or goal. This statement may or may not come from a KJ Chart or Interrelationship Digraph.

      Note: Unlike the KJ Method, the Tree Diagram becomes more effective as the issue is more clearly specified. This is important since the emphasis is on finding the logical and sequential links between ideas/tasks and not pure creativity.

2. Once the statement is agreed upon, the team must generate all of the possible tasks, methods, or causes related to that statement. These could follow three different formats:

    a. Use the cards from the KJ Chart as a foundation. For example, you might take the 10 - 20 cards that fall under one broad heading as a starting point.

    b. Brainstorm all of the possible tasks/methods/ causes and record them on a flip chart. These ideas could then be placed on individual cards or rearranged on the flip chart.

    c. Brainstorm as in "b" but record directly onto cards for continued use.

        Note: When brainstorming, continue to apply to each idea the question "In order to achieve X, what must happen or exist?" Or "What has happened or what exists that causes X?"

3. Evaluate and code all of the ideas with the following code:

    O   Possible to carry out
    ^   Need more information to see if possible
    X   Impossible to carry out

    Note: Code an idea to be impossible only after very careful consideration. "Impossible" must not be equated with "we've never done it before".

4. Construct the actual Tree Diagram:

    a. Place the central goal/issue card to the left of a flip chart or table. (The remainder of the instructions will assume that cards are being used, but the same steps would apply if the chart is drawn directly on the flip chart.)

    b. Ask the question, "What method or task do we need to complete in order to accomplish this goal or purpose?"

Find the ideas on the cards or flip chart list that are most closely related to that statement. These may also be viewed as those tasks that are the closest in terms of sequence or cause & effect.

c. Place the ideas/tasks from "b" immediately to the right of the central issue card as you would in a family tree or organizational chart.

d. The ideas/tasks from "c" now become the focal point. In other words, the question from "b" is repeated and the remaining cards are again sorted to be placed to the right as the next row in the Tree. This process is repeated until all of the cards or recorded ideas are exhausted.
    Note: If none of the cards answer the repeated question, create a new one and place it in the proper spot.

e. Review the entire Tree Diagram to ensure that there are no obvious gaps in sequence or logic. Check this by reviewing each path, starting at the most basic task to the extreme right. Ask of each idea/task, "If we do Y, will it lead to the accomplishment of this next idea/task?"

f. Review with other groups for relevant input and revise where needed.

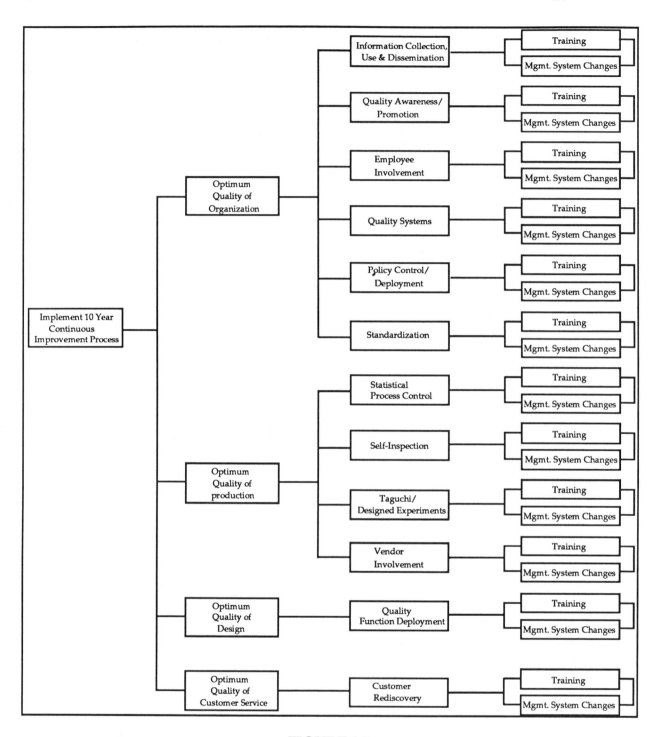

FIGURE 4.3

MATRIX DIAGRAM

Definition

This tool organizes large groups of characteristics, functions, and tasks in such a way that logical connecting points between each are graphically displayed. It also shows the importance of each connecting point relative to every other correlation.

Of the tools discussed thus far (KJ Method, Interrelationship Digraph, System Flow/Tree Diagram), the Matrix Diagram has enjoyed the widest use. It is based on the principle that whenever a series of items are placed in a line (horizontal) and another series of items are placed in a row (vertical) there will be intersecting points that indicate a relationship. Furthermore, the Matrix Diagram features highly visible symbols that indicate the strength of the relationship between the items that intersect at that point. The Matrix Diagram is very similar to the other tools in that new cumulative patterns of relationships emerge based on the interaction between individual items. Even in this most logical process, unforeseen patterns "just happen".

When to Use the Matrix Diagram

Because the Matrix Diagram has enjoyed the widest use of the New Tools, it has evolved into a number of forms. The key to successfully applying a Matrix Diagram is choosing the right format matrix for the situation. The following are the most commonly used matrix forms:

1.   **L Shaped Matrix Diagram**
          This is the most basic form of Matrix Diagram. In the L shape, two interrelated groups of items are presented in line and row format. It is a simple two-dimensional representation that shows the inter-section of related pairs of items as shown in Figure M-1. The Matrix Diagram may be used to display relationships between items in countless operational areas such as administration, manufacturing, personnel, R&D, etc.

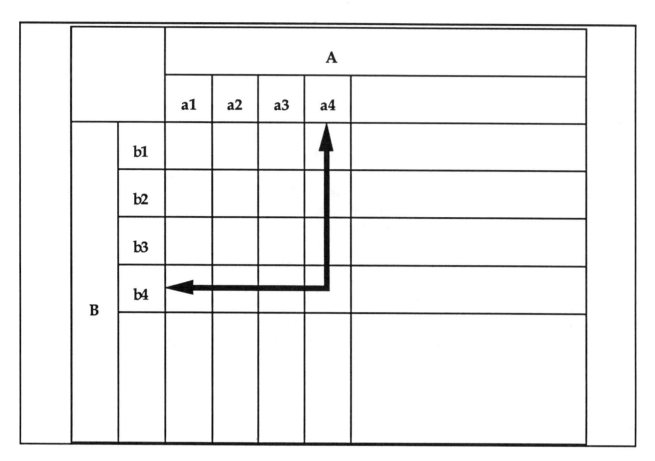

FIGURE M-1: L Shaped Matrix

In Chart M-1, the Matrix Diagram is used to identify
all of the organizational tasks that need to be accomplished
and how they should be allocated to individuals.
NOTE: It is doubly interesting if each person
completes the matrix individually and then compares
the coding with everyone in the work group.

◎ Primary Responsibility
○ Secondary Responsibility   **+ Slightly More Emphasis**
△ Communications/Need to Know

	Bob	Mike	Lee	Larry	Ann	Pat	Lynn	Board of Dir.	Other			
Administration												
Payroll	◎		△				○	△				
Benefits	○	△	◎	△	△	△	△	○				
Office Systems	○	○	◎			◎	△					
Computer Programs	○	△	◎			○	○					
Courses												
Update Mailing List			○			◎	◎					
Select Courses to be Offered	◎	◎	◎			△	△		△ Deming			
Approve Course Content	◎	◎	○			△			△ Deming	○ Instructor		
Prepare Brochures	○	○	○		◎	△			○ Instructor			
Prepare Mailing			△			◎	○					
Hotel Arrangments	△	△	◎			△⁺	△					
Order Materials	△	△	◎			○	△					
Register People	△	△	△			◎	○					
Copy Materials	△	△	△			◎	○					
Prepare Packets	△	△	△			◎	○					
Room Set-Up	◎	◎	◎									
Post Receipts	△		◎				◎					
Prepare Bills												
New Course Development												
Market Research	○	△	△			△						
Implementing Deming	◎	◎	△	○		△	○					
TQC	◎	○	△									
Fundraising												
Annual Reports	○	○	○		◎	○	△					
Corporate Donations	◎	○	○	◎	○							
Committees												
Program Planning	◎	○	△			△						
Statistical Resources	○	◎	△	△	△	△						
TQC	◎	○	△	△	△	△						
Supplier Institute	○	○⁺			◎							

CHART M-1: L Shaped Matrix

Chart M-2 shows yet another application to an all-too-common problem: shipping problems. By brain-storming all of the possible reasons for shipping problems it is very clear that the "shipping" problem

does not rest only with the shipping department. The
matrix forces the participants to also develop the list
of all related departments. The interrelationship
between these two sets of items points to the pattern of
responsibility for solution to the problems.

Problems / Department/Individually/Function	Customer Service	Quality	Production	Scheduling	Process Engineering	Shipping	Design Engineering
Missing Parts	△		○			◎	
Does Not Meet Specs	△	○	◎		○		△
Wrong Parts	△	○		○		◎	
Mis-labeled	△		◎			○	
Defective Parts	△	○	◎		○		△
Arrived Late	△		○	◎		○	
Too Many	△		○			◎	
Too Few	△		○			◎	
Shipping Damage	△					◎	○
Wrong Part Ordered	◎						
Customer No Longer Needs Part	◎						
Cannot Process Part	△	○	○		◎		◎

◎ Primary Responsibility

○ Secondary Responsibility

△ Communications/Receive Reports

CHART M-2: L Shaped Matrix

2.   **T Shaped Matrix**
          The T Shaped Matrix is nothing more than the
combination of two L Shaped Matrix diagrams. As
shown in Figure M-2, the T Shaped Matrix is based on the
premise that two separate sets of items are both related
to a third set. Therefore, A items are somehow related to
both B and C items.

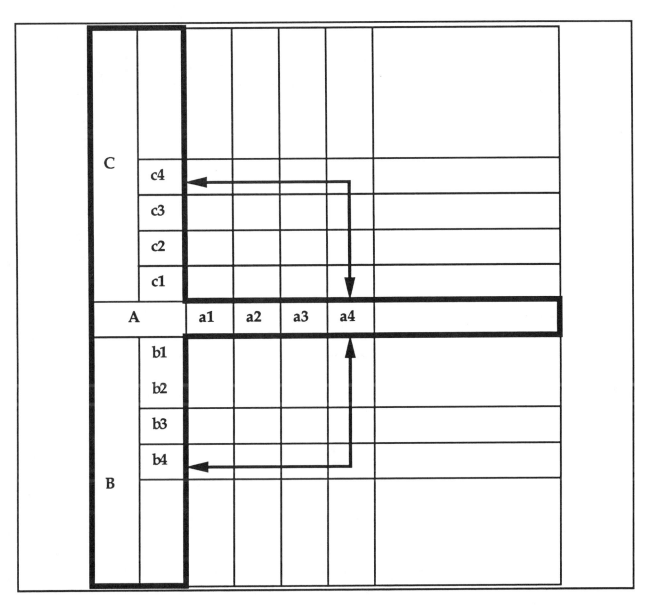

FIGURE M-2: T Shaped Matrix

Chart M-3 shows one application. In this case, it shows
the relationship between a set of courses in a
curriculum and two important sets of considerations:
Who should do the training for each course? And,
who would be the most appropriate attendees for each
of the courses?

Who Trains?

	SQC	7 Old Tools	7 New Tools	Reliability	Design Review	QC Basics	QCC Facilitator	Diagnostic Tools	Problem Solving	Communication Skills	Organize for Quality	Design of Experiment	Company Mission	Quality Planning	Just in Time	New Superv. Training	Comp. Tot. Q. Mgt. Syst.	Group Dynamics Skills	SQC Course/Execs.
Human Resource Dept.																			
Managers																			
Operators																			
Consultants																			
Production operator																			
Craft foremen																			
GLSPC Coordinator																			
Plant SPC Coordinator																			
University																			
Technology specialists																			
Engineers																			

Need to tailor to groups

X = Full
O = Overview

Who Attends?

Courses	SQC	7 Old Tools	7 New Tools	Reliability	Design Review	QC Basics	QCC Facilitator	Diagnostic Tools	Problem Solving	Communication Skills	Organize for Quality	Design of Experiment	Company Mission	Quality Planning	Just in Time	New Superv. Training	Comp. Tot. Q. Mgt. Syst.	Group Dynamics Skills	SQC Course/Execs.
Executives																			
Top Mgmt.																			
Middle Mgmt.																			
Prod. Supervisors																			
Supp. Func. Mgrs.																			
Staff																			
Marketing																			
Sales																			
Engineers																			
Clerical																			
Prod. Worker																			
Qual. Professional																			
Project Team																			
Emp. Involv. Teams																			
Suppliers																			
Maintenance																			

CHART M-3: T-Matrix Diagram on Company-Wide Training

The T Shaped Matrix has also been widely used to develop new materials by simultaneously relating different, alternative materials to two sets of desirable properties.

3.   **Y Shaped Matrix**

The Y Shaped Matrix simply allows the user to combine and compare three sets of items to each other. As shown in Figure M-3, it is clear that you can now determine the interaction between items in Group A with those in Group B, as well as Group B with Group C and Group C with Group A.   This is invaluable when comparing product characteristics, etc.

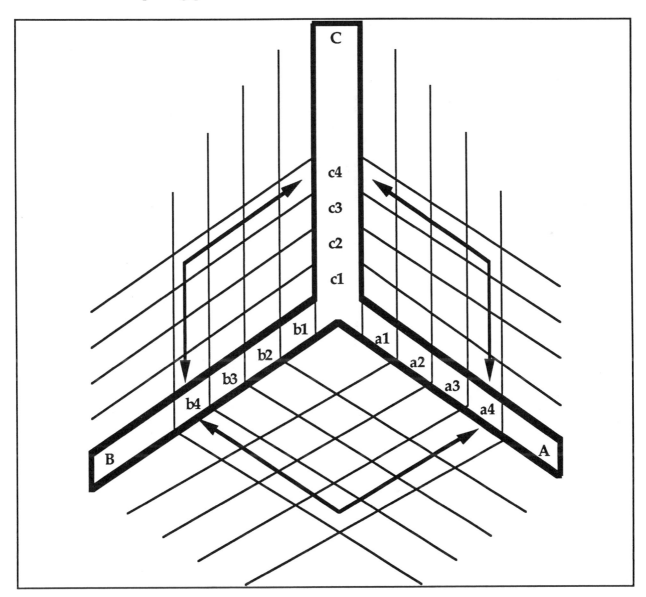

FIGURE M-3: Y Shaped Matrix

4.   **X Shaped Matrix**
     The X Shaped Matrix is a format that is rarely
used. It shows the interaction between four sets of
items. In Figure M-4, it graphically related A&B,
B&C, C&D, and D&A. It is available but its use is not
well documented.

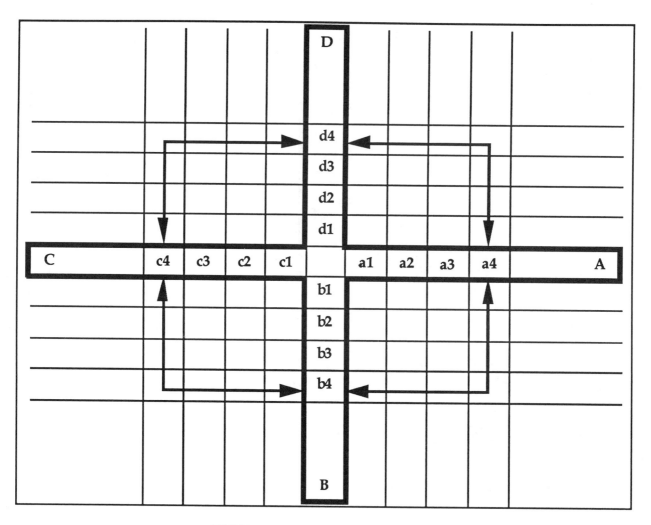

FIGURE M-4: X Shaped Matrix

5.   **C Shaped Matrix**
        The C Shaped Matrix (or Cubic Type Matrix)
makes it possible to visually represent the intersection
of three interrelated sets of items.

        Other matrix diagram formats allow you to
show the relationship between three or even four sets
of items. In effect, however, they only compare two
sets of items at a time with any connections to a
third set only by inference. In other words, A is
connected with B, and B is connected with C, so it can be
inferred that A is related in some way to C.

        The advantage of the C Shaped Matrix is that it
can graphically display the connection between A, B,
and C directly as one converging point.

Chart M-4 shows a C Shaped Matrix displaying the interaction between Layout, Software, and Hardware items. In this case, there is a strong connection between 4 under Layout (Select Software), 13 under Hardware (Measure Row Materials), and 9 under Software (Be Flexible Against Changes).

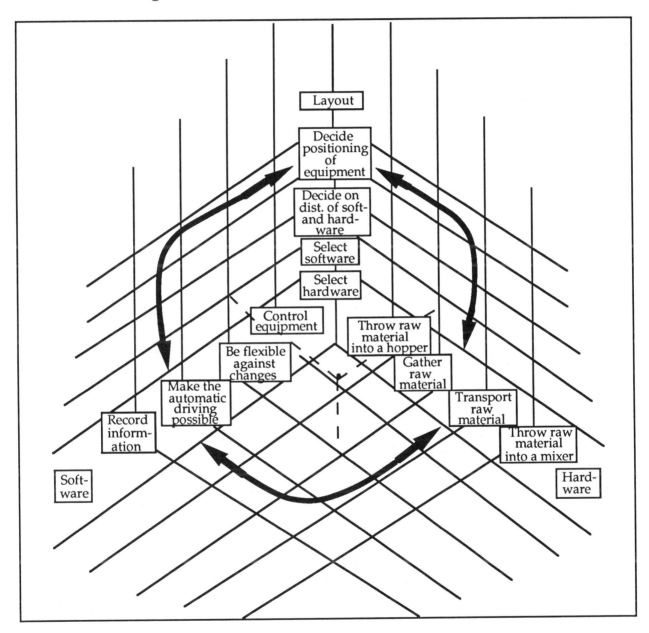

CHART M-4: C Shape Matrix

6.   **Combination Matrix/Tree Diagram**
        Generating the most complete set of items
possible is as important as selecting the right format
matrix. The Tree Diagram is widely used to generate
the tasks, ideas and/or characteristics that form one or
more sides of the matrix.

        Figure M-5 shows two tree diagrams that have
been merged into a simple L Shaped Matrix. Even
more common than this is using a tree diagram to
create a set of tasks to be accomplished (vertical axis
of matrix) and merge them in an L Shaped Matrix with
all of the departments/functions (horizontal axis).
The degrees of responsibility for each task can then be
clearly allocated and indicated.

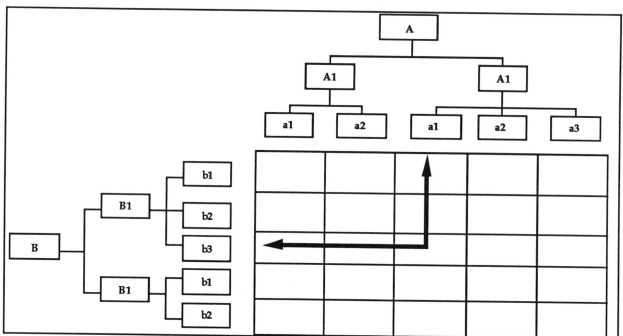

FIGURE M-5: Combination of Matrix and Tree Diagram

Construction of a Matrix Diagram

The process of constructing any of the various format Matrix
Diagrams is very straightforward. It as as follows:

1.   Generate the two, three, or four sets of items that will
        be compared in the appropriate matrix.
        NOTE: These often emerge from the last row of
        detail in a Tree Diagram. This is the most effective
        method, but the matrix has proven helpful when

based upon brainstormed items from a knowledge team.

2.   Determine the proper matrix format.
     The choice of sets of items to compare is based on an educated guess and experience. It is trial and error. Don't be afraid to abandon or modify a line of reasoning.

3.   Place the sets of items in such a way as to form the axes of the matrix.
     If these items come from one or more Tree Diagrams you can simply tape the cards (if used) on a flip chart pad. Otherwise you can simply record them directly on the pad. Finally, draw the lines which will form the boxes within which the appropriate relationship symbols will be placed (see step 4).

4.   Decide on the relationship symbols to be used. The following are the most common, but use your imagination.

     •   Function Responsibility Chart

         ◎   Primary Responsibility

         ○   Secondary Responsibility

         △   Should Receive Information

     •   Quality Characteristics Chart
         A Most Critical
         B More Critical
         C Critical

     •   Product Testing Chart
         • Test In Process
         O Test Scheduled
         X Test & Evaluation Possible

Note: Regardless of which symbols you choose to use, be sure to include a legend that prominently displays the relationship symbols and their meanings.

MATRIX DATA ANALYSIS

Definition

To arrange data displayed in a Matix Diagram so that it can be more easily viewed and reveal the true strength of the relationship between variables.

When to Use Matrix Data Analysis

Matrix Data Analysis is primarily used for market research, planning and development of new products, and process analysis. It is used to determine the representative characteristics of each variable being examined. For example, what are the demographic characteristics of groups of people who like or dislike certain foods? What are the representative characteristics of a new cloth given an array of possible end uses?

Construction of a Matrix Data Analysis Chart

1. In order to find the "representative characteristics" of a product or consumer, use the "Principal Component Analysis Method". It is a formula that mathematically calculates the impact a factor has on the process.

2. Compare data among evaluation groups showing how much of the intergroup variation is due to a particular characteristic of that group (or combination thereof).

3. Calculate the cumulative contribution rates of the principle components to the overall ratings (e.g., sex, age, and occupation accounted for 75% of the variability in the rating).

4. Display the distribution of results graphically in a four quadrant graph.

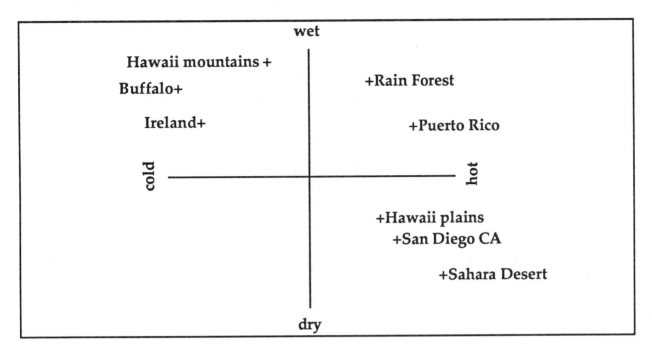

Illustration of Matrix Data Analysis Using Weather
FIGURE 4.4

Illustration of Matrix Data Analysis Using Pain Relievers
FIGURE 4.5

Process Decision Program Chart (PDPC)

Definition

Process Decision Program Chart (PDPC) is a method which maps out every conceivable event and contingency that can occur when moving from a problem statement to possible solutions. This tool is used to plan each possible chain of events that needs to occur when the problem or goal is an unfamiliar one.

The underlying principle behind the PDPC is that the path toward virtually any goal is filled with uncertainty and an imperfect environment. If this weren't true, we would have a Deming "sequence" like the following:

$$\textbf{PLAN} \text{ ------------>} \quad \textbf{DO}$$

Reality makes the Deming Cycle a necessity.

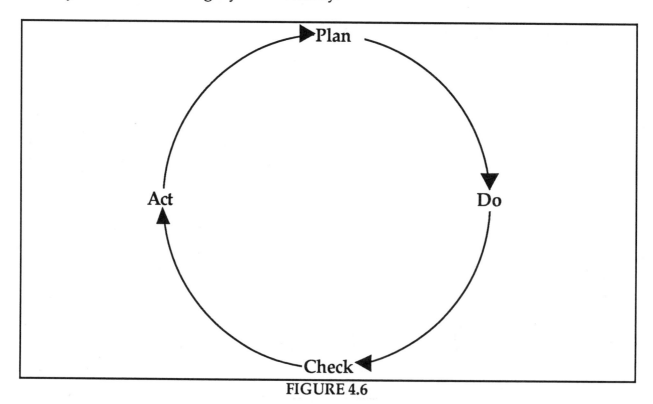

FIGURE 4.6

PDPC anticipates the unexpected and, in a sense, attempts to "short circuit" the cycle so that the "check" takes place during a dry-run of the process. The beauty of PDPC is that it not only tries to anticipate deviations, but also to develop countermeasures that will either:

a.   prevent the deviation from occurring
b.   be in place in case the deviation occurs

The first option is ideal in that it is truly preventive. However, we live in a world of limited resources. In allocating these resources we have to often "play the odds" as to the chance of X,Y, or Z happening. Given that fact, the next best thing is to have a contingency plan in place when a case that we were "betting against" occurs. PDPC provides a structure to go in either direction.

When to Use a PDPC

An ideal use of a PDPC would be as follows:

> A scientist's goal is to explore the core of the earth to determine its composition. Her plan is to dig a tunnel four miles deep. It's never been done, she doesn't know how long it will take, but she has to make a funding proposal. The questions are: How do you describe all of the possible paths to achieve this goal? How do you know what some of the obstacles will be? How can you prevent these possibilities from becoming realities? If obstacles do occur, how do you react in a timely way so as to avoid going back to "square one?" A cost estimate will be possible only if these questions have been answered. How can this be done systematically? Simple . . . . PDPC!

It is obviously not so simple, but it certainly provides a methodical structure that can prevent details from slipping between the cracks.
NOTE: PDPC is like the Tree Diagram in structure and aim since both deal with possible patterns of methods and plans. In the same vein, it is closely tied to methods in reliability engineering such as Failure Mode & Effect Analysis (FMEA) and Fault Tree Analysis (FTA).

The prime difference between these two formats is that FMEA starts from the smallest detail (sub-system) and assesses the probability of failure at any step. Also, it determines the cumulative impact on the end goal. FTA, on the other hand, starts with an undesirable result and then traces it back sequentially looking for the cause. PDPC is enjoying widespread use in particular because of the stress on product liability.

Construction of a Process Decision Program Chart (PDPC)

Even though PDPC is a methodical process it has few guidelines in terms of the process and finished product. The most important thing to keep in mind is that you must get to the point where deviations and contingencies are **clearly** indicated. This must be true at every level of detail in the chart.

Note 1: The source of the goal statement that starts the PDPC process often emerges from tools such as the KJ, Interrelationship Digraph, or even the Tree Diagram. As is true of all the other tools, PDPC can also be used effectively on its own.

Note 2: One word of caution. **EXPLOSION!** This is how some users have described PDPC. The creation of possible paths and countermeasures can multiply the complexity of the chart tremendously. Don't let it overwhelm you. Break the material into bite-size pieces, develop each piece, and then reassemble the final product.

The following seems to be the most workable approach:

a.   Follow the instructions for the Tree Diagram through to the end.

b.   Take one branch of the Tree Diagram (starting from the "purpose" in the row to the immediate right of the "ultimate goal/purpose") and ask the questions: What could go wrong at this step? or What other path could this step take?
Note: It is easier if the items in that original branch are on cards so that they can be moved easily. This is important because you are inserting problems and countermeasures into an existing sequence.

c.   Answer the questions in "b" by branching off the original path.

d.   Off to the side of that step, list actions/countermeasures that could be taken. These are normally enclosed in "clouds" similar to cartoon captions and attached to that problem statement.

e.   Continue the process until that original branch is exhausted.

f.   Repeat "b" through "e" on the next most important tree branch, etc.

g.   Assemble the individual branches into a final PDPC, review with the proper team of people, and adjust as needed.

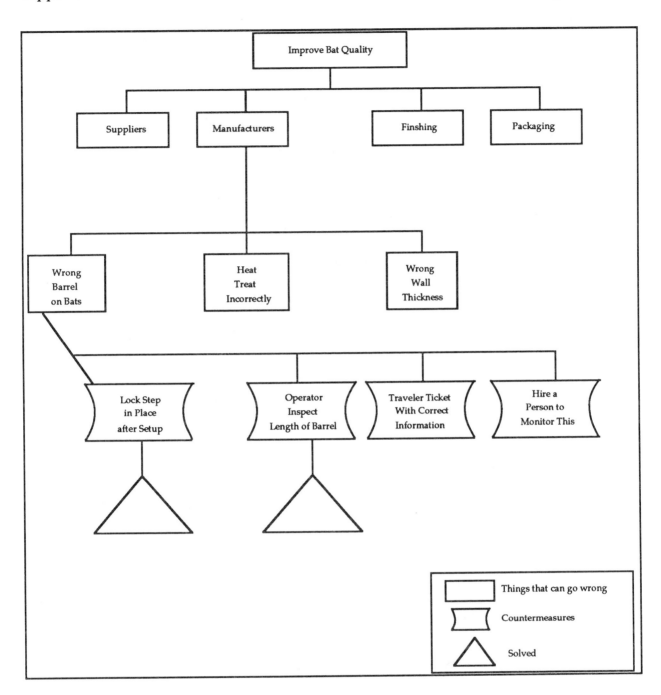

Process Decision Program Chart (PDPC)
FIGURE 4.7

PDPC of PLAN

STEPS
1. IDENTIFY NEEDS (CUSTOMER)
2. SELECT EQUIPMENT
3. TRAIN EMPLOYEES
4. INSTALL EQUIPMENT
5. HAPPY CUSTOMERS

PROBLEMS
3.0 TRAINING
3.1 NO DEMONSTRATION EQUIPMENT
3.2 EMPLOYEE APATHY
3.3 NOT ENOUGH TIME
3.4 NO MANUALS
3.5 TRAINING TOO LATE
3.6 TRAINING TOO EARLY

COUNTERMEASURES
3.2.0 EMPLOYEE APATHY
3.2.1 MORE MONEY
3.2.2 NO LAYOFFS
3.2.3 FIRE THEM
*3.2.4 BETTER MANAGEMENT
**3.2.5 BIG PICTURE

ARROW DIAGRAM

Definition

This tool is used to plan the most appropriate schedule for any task and to control the task effectively as it progresses. This tool is closely related to the CPM and PERT Diagram methods. It is used when the task at hand is a familiar one with sub-tasks that are of a known duration.

The Arrow Diagram is one tool that is certainly not Japanese. It is based on the Program Evaluation and Review Technique (PERT) which was developed in the U.S. after WWII to speed the development of the Polaris program. The Arrow Diagram removes some of the "black box magic" from the traditional PERT process. This is consistent with the general idea that the key to Japanese success is their ability to take previously available tools and make them accessible to the larger population. So, instead of industrial, manufacturing, and design engineers papering their walls with PERT charts (which they have done), they can be used as a daily tool throughout the organization.

When to Use the Arrow Diagram

The most important criterion (and perhaps the only meaningful one) is that the sub-tasks, their sequencing, and their duration must be well known. If this is not the case, then the construction of the Arrow Diagram can become a very frustrating experience. When the timing of the actual events is very different from the Arrow Diagram, people dismiss the Arrow Diagram as a nuisance, never to be used again. When there is a lack of process history, the PDPC is usually a much more helpful tool.

Note: Don't be afraid to admit that you don't know everything there is to know about a process. It is better to decide on the proper tasks and sequencing than to pretend that you have a handle on the scheduling dimension.

Obviously, there are many processes that do have a well documented history. Therefore, the Arrow Diagram has enjoyed widespread use in such areas as:

- New Product Development
- Construction Projects
- Marketing Plans
- Complex Negotiations

Construction of an Arrow Diagram

As usual, a successful process is based on having complete input from the right sources. It's possible that one person could have all of the needed information for structuring an Arrow Diagram, but it is highly unlikely. Therefore, assembling a team of the right people is usually the first step. This team would follow the steps listed below:

1.   Generate and record all of the necessary tasks to complete the project.
      Note 1: It is strongly recommended that these tasks be written simply and clearly on cards (about business card size or slightly narrower). This is essential for moving the cards before the final lines and arrows are drawn. Expect to generate 50 - 100 such cards.
      Note 2: On the Job Cards be sure to write the task to be completed only in the top half of the card. Draw a line under the task, thereby dividing the card in half. The length of time to complete that task will be put in this space later.

2.   Scatter the completed job cards and judge the inter-relationship between jobs. Determine the relationship among the cards (i.e., what **precedes, follows,** or is **simultaneous** to each job), and place them in the proper flow. Delete duplications and add new cards if jobs are overlooked.

3.   Decide on the positions of the cards by finding the path with the most job cards in a series. Leave space between the cards so that "nodes" can be added later. (Nodes are the symbols that show the beginning and end of a task or event. Draw these in only when the various paths have been determined.)

4.   Find the cards whose path parallels the first path, then the path that parallels that one, etc.

5.   Once these paths are finalized, write in the nodes, number them, and add arrows between tasks in each path as well as those linking each path to the other.
      Note: Each task/job is made up of two nodes. The task that begins with node #1 and ends with node #2 is task 1, 2.

6.   Carefully study the number of days, hours, weeks, etc. for each task and complete each job card.

7.   Based on #5, calculate the earliest and latest start time for each node.
Note 1: This is critical if you are to calculate the Critical Path (as in CPM), which is the longest cumulative time that the tasks require. This is therefore the shortest time in which one could expect the final tasks to be completed.
Note 2: The earliest and latest start times should be calculated using the following formulas:

1.   a. **Earliest Node Time**
Suppose there is a job that starts from the node i. "Earliest node time" is the day when the job can be started. It is expressed as t_i^E.

    b. **Latest Node Time**
Suppose there is a job that ends at the node i. "Latest node time" is the day when the job must be finished. It is expressed as t_i^L. t_i^E and t_i^L will be written near the node.

2.   **How to Calculate Earliest Node Time**

Here is how to calculate earliest node time:

a. Earliest node time of the starting point (node 1) in the arrow diagram is 0 (i.e., $t_j^E = 0$).

b. When one job has a latter node j, its earliest node date t_i^E can be obtained using the following equation.

$$t_j^E = t_i^E + D_{ij}$$

Where t_i^E is earliest node time of starting node i of node j. D_{ij} is the necessary days of the job (i,j).

c. When there are two or more jobs using the node j as their latter node, its earliest node time t_j^E can be obtained using the following equation.

$$t_j^E = \max(t_i^E + D_{ij})$$

3.   **How to Calculate Latest Node Time**

   a. Latest node time of the very last point (node n) in the arrow diagram has the same value as earliest node time of that node, i.e.,

$$t_n^L = t_n^E$$

   b. When there is one job using node i as the starting node, its latest node time t_i^L can be obtained using the following equation.

$$t_i^L = t_j^T - D_{ij}$$

   Where t_j^L is latest node time of following node j to the node i. D_{ij} is the necessary days for the job (i,j).

   c. When there are more than two jobs which use node i as a preceding node, its latest node time t_i^L can be obtained using the following equation.

$$t_i^L = \min (t_j^L - D_{ij})$$

4.   Determine the relationship between t_i^E and latest node time t_i^L at the same node.

$$t_i^E = t_i^L$$

   There is the following relationship between earliest node time t_i^E and latest node time t_i^L at the same node.

$$t_i^E = t_i^L$$

5.   **Critical Path**

   Critical path is the longest path from the starting point to the finishing point on the arrow diagram. It is the series of jobs important to the schedule control. Critical path should be as shown in the following equation.

$$t_i^E = t_i^L$$

   Along the path, t_i^E and t_i^L should be posted, and the path should be shown in a heavy directional line in the arrow diagram.

SYMBOLS

1.   **Event, node:** these are the beginning
      and the finish of a job, and they are the
      connecting points to other jobs.

2.   **Job, activity:** this is the element that
      needs a length of time.

3.   **Dummy:** this is the element that shows
      the interrelationship between jobs, but
      needs no time.

4.   **Numbers for nodes**: these are the
      numbers at the nodes or events, and they
      show which job is being referred to, or in what
      order it is placed.

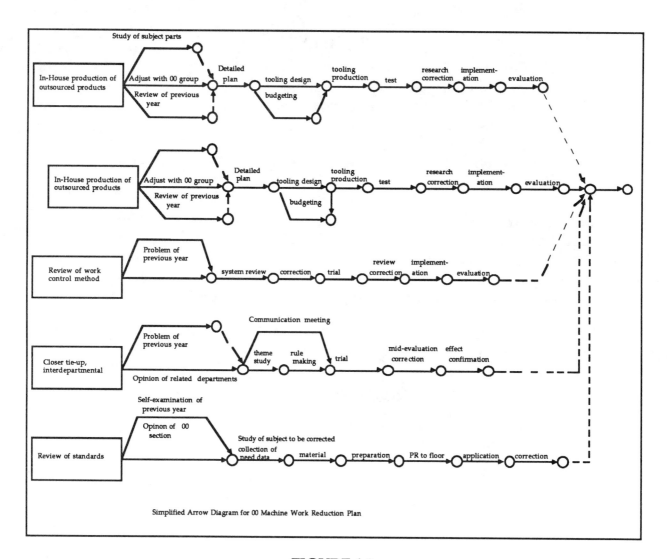

FIGURE 4.8

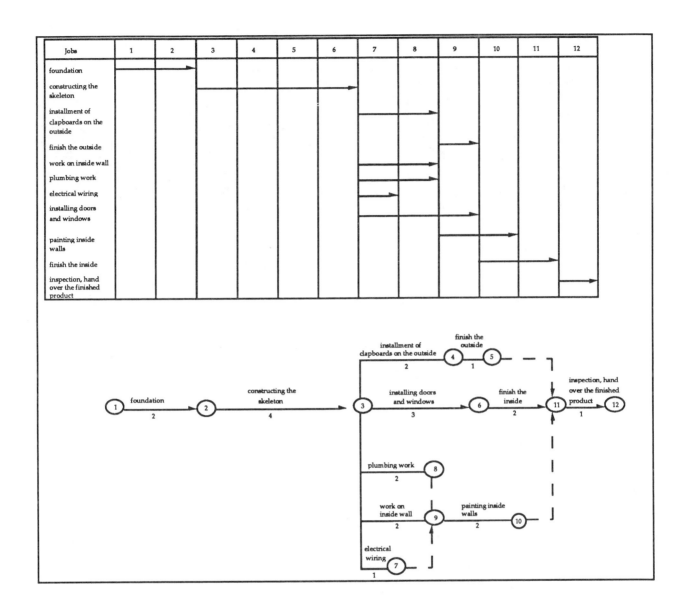

GANT CHART vs. ARROW DIAGRAM
FIGURE 4.9